The Mums' Book of Glamour

The Mums' Book of Glamour

How to be Fabulous

Veena Bhairo-Smith

Michael O'Mara Books Limited

First published in Great Britain in 2010 by
Michael O'Mara Books Limited
9 Lion Yard
Tremadoc Road
London SW4 7NQ

Papers used by Michael O'Mara Books Limited are natural, recyclable products made from wood grown in sustainable forests. The manufacturing processes conform to the environmental regulations of the country of origin.

A CIP catalogue record for this book is available from the British Library.

ISBN: 978-1-84317-371-7

1 3 5 7 9 10 8 6 4 2

www.mombooks.com

Cover design by Blacksheep Design
Text design and typesetting by K.DESIGN, Winscombe, Somerset
Illustrations by Robyn Neild

Printed and bound in Great Britain by Clays Ltd, St Ives plc

For my ever-so-glamorous Mummy, Tanya and Nanny,
my wonderful Daddy, and my darlings Sonny,
Evie and Adrian

Contents

CONTENTS

CONTENTS

CONTENTS

Introduction

Let's face it: being a mum is one of the most rewarding jobs in life, but it can really take it out of you – the Razzle-Dazzle, that is. We all have it, but somewhere along the way it gets buried under the seemingly endless cycle of washing, cooking, ironing, cleaning, homework and school runs ... not to mention the arguing, tantrums and backchat.

But once in a while you need to stop, pull yourself up to your full height and take stock of who you are under that mountain of Mum Tasks. We are all capable of looking gorgeous, feeling relaxed and exuding confidence, but it just takes time – a luxury most of us mums don't have – to slow down, glam up and let all those qualities shine through.

Whether you have limited time, know-how, or simply a limited budget, this book will provide you with all the tips and tricks you need to reveal your fabulous side. You may be new to motherhood and wondering whether life will ever be the same again, or perhaps you're an experienced mum who can't actually remember what life was like BFK (before kids). No matter what your circumstances, this book will inspire and encourage you to make the most of every opportunity – because, ladies, there is a whole world of fabulousness out there.

As you work your way through this book, bear in mind the four very simple principles of glamorous mumhood:

1. **Don't try to recreate the life you had BFK.** That was then, when you had all the time in the world to get ready for a night out or could manage a blow-dry before work; nowadays an uninterrupted shower is a luxury. It's time to move on and embrace the new, wonderful chapter in your life.

2. **Think practically about the time you can spare to focus on yourself.** Whether it's five minutes or half an hour, devise a routine that will work for you. Life can be all that it was BFK and much, much more, but it just requires some considered time-management and a spot of forward planning.

3. **Don't overlook the hundreds of little things that combine to create a glamorous persona.** Know your best asset and how to enhance it – a striking necklace on your elegant neck, a splash of colour on your full lips, polished nails on your graceful hands. Even if you only have five minutes to

spare, work with your best attribute. One or two changes may be all it takes to make others notice your fabulousness at the school gates or at work, and a smile or a spritz of perfume could be one of them – easy!

4. **Remember that confidence and positive thinking can transform a harassed mother into a gorgeous goddess.** Eating the right foods, getting enough sleep, maintaining good friendships or having a soak in the tub are all achievable yet invaluable tools in the fight against unfabulousness.

So set aside some time each day to read the gems contained in this book and you'll soon be unleashing that dormant glamour puss inside you …

Take a Long, Hard Look in the Mirror

Glamming up your look is of course not the only way to be fabulous, but it's certainly a good place to start. These first few chapters will address various facets of outward appearance, from make-up and fashion to mental and physical wellbeing.

First things first, though: before you go on a mad spending spree, it's important to know what suits you and what will really enhance your best physical assets. After all, there's no point in buying the latest fashions if they're just not going to work with your shape or colouring. Understanding what suits you, and getting to grips with the advantages and limitations of your skin and hair types, is a process that can take an awful lot of trial and error. Most women will only need to look back at photos of their teenage years to appreciate this.

In short, the only way to get the most out of your precious time on the high street is to develop a positive acceptance of your appearance. But, as we all know, that is often easier said than done ...

THE GRASS IS ALWAYS GREENER ...

It's a sad fact of human nature that we're forever comparing ourselves unfavourably with other people; wasting time in this manner is one of the biggest obstacles to making the most of what we *do* have. There'll always be someone with smoother skin or straighter hair or an annoyingly petite waist; when it comes to looking good, half the battle is having the confidence just to get on with it without putting yourself down.

STYLE VS. FASHION

Another obstacle is the fact that fashion is so often confused with style. Fashions come and go – frequently they look ghastly and entirely unbecoming on 90 per cent of the population – and are as changeable and contradictory as the seasons. Style, on the other hand, is a realistic understanding of which fashions looks good on you and what sort of outfits and accessories you can legitimately carry off.

Some people are blessed with natural style and know-how. But the truth is that style is not an exclusive club. Everybody is capable of having great style, but style requires confidence – and confidence, which we will come to on p.124, is all about being honest with yourself. So find the nearest full-length mirror and let's take a good, hard look at you ...

10-STEP 'GETTING TO KNOW YOU' GUIDE

1. What's your body shape?

No matter what your body type or shape, it has the potential to look absolutely gorgeous. So many of us have spent years trying to be super-skinny when it just isn't what nature intended for everyone; likewise, the super-skinny bemoan their small boobs or shapeless legs and everybody just wastes time wishing they had other people's body parts.

The key is knowing what shape you are, accepting it and learning to treat it with respect, as well as understanding what works well for you in terms of clothes, food and exercise.

Once you have mastered these points you will be well on your way to a 'body beautiful'.

There are three basic body-classification types. Try to work out which one best describes you.

Endomorph: You tend to have bigger bones than other body types, and may well describe yourself as 'stocky'. Your face is most likely round and you might have 'child-bearing hips'. Arms and legs tend to be fairly short, while hands and feet are small. You have higher levels of body fat and have a harder time losing weight than the other body types, but it's much easier for you to build muscle.

Mesomorph: You may have a more athletic build and can gain muscle quite easily. You could either have curves or a straight physique, and might also have broad shoulders with a narrow waist. Your metabolism is fast and you can lose weight easily.

Ectomorph: Your figure is most likely to be thin or straight. There may not be much difference in girth between your waist, hips and shoulders. You can lose weight quite easily and probably have low levels of body fat, but it is harder for you to gain muscle.

As well as these three body types, there are four common body shapes. Which one best describes you?

Hourglass: Your upper body and lower body are in good proportion to one other, and you are likely to have a narrow waist. You may have a tendency to gain weight all over, but particularly on your hips and chest. You are more than likely an endomorph or a mesomorph.

Pear: Your lower body is larger than your upper body, and your hips may be wider than your shoulders. You have a tendency to gain weight below the waist and have a small chest and flat stomach. You are more than likely a mesomorph.

Apple: Your upper body is generally bigger than your lower body. You commonly have slim hips but a large chest and stomach. You tend to gain weight above the waist or around the backside. You are more than likely to be a mesomorph or endomorph.

Ruler: You may be waiflike, slim or straight with hardly any difference in girth between your hips, waist and shoulders. Fat tends to head for your stomach and backside, while your legs and arms remain slim. You are more than likely an ectomorph.

There are no hard-and-fast rules here, so it doesn't really matter if you don't seem to fit one type perfectly. You may identify with a combination of types and that is perfectly normal, but it's good to know these traits exist – especially if you've been trying unsuccessfully to lose weight for a number of years.

There's more on body types and fashion on p.80, and on body-type-specific exercise on p.110.

2. What's your skin type?

Our skin type is determined by how much or how little sebum (oil) our skin produces, which in turn is related to our genetic make-up, our diet, our stress levels, our environment, our medication and our skincare regime. Rather like snowflakes, no two skin types are exactly the same, since it's all bound up in our unique DNA, but dermatologists have created five main skin-type categories for the sake of product-labelling convenience.

Before we get to the five categories, however, you might like to try this quick test. Wash your face and pat it dry with a towel. Take a sheet of rice paper or blotting paper and hold it close to your face, pressing it gently. Does it stick?

YES	You have oily skin
STICKS TO YOUR T-ZONE (across your forehead and down your nose)	You have combination or normal skin
NO	You have dry skin

These three basic skin types and the two additional types are listed below. As with body types, don't worry if you don't fit neatly into one category: some people belong to two or three.

Oily: This means your production of sebum is a bit over the top, which can cause your skin to look shiny and sometimes feel greasy to touch. Your pores are large and can easily become blocked, so you may be prone to blackheads and blemishes.

Normal/Combination: Your skin has a fresh, clear appearance and may be firm to touch with good elasticity (i.e. it springs back when you touch it). It has a smooth, even texture with medium-sized pores. Alternatively, the skin on your cheeks might be dry while your T-zone is slightly oily.

Dry: Your sebum production is insufficient and your skin may feel tight as a result, especially after cleansing. You are more prone to fine wrinkles and the signs of ageing, and can have flaky skin with poor elasticity.

Sensitive: Unfortunately, sensitive skin is an ever-growing problem, with over 60 per cent of people having suffered somewhere along the way. The key to looking after sensitive skin is to expose your skin to as few products as possible; by minimizing the number of chemical ingredients you slap on, you limit the number of reactions your skin can have.

Ageing/Sun-damaged: Your skin will feel taut most of the time and you might have visible wrinkles. Your skin will be slack around the cheek and jaw-line.

HOW TO TAKE CARE OF YOUR SKIN

Whichever category you fall into, it's important to take care of your skin and develop a regime that suits you. For years, cosmetic companies have drilled home the three-step process – cleanse, tone, moisturize – as being vital to healthy, younger-looking skin. More recently, however, the role of toner has been thrown into question. Many top skincare gurus argue that toners can also strip away natural lipids (fats that help keep the skin moist). This is because many toners are alcohol-based, which means they're severe on certain skin types; contrary to what you might think, they are especially bad for oily skin. So if you're not getting the desired results through the traditional cleanse-tone-moisturize procedure, try leaving the toner out and see what difference that makes. Alternatively, try a gentler, non-alcohol-based toner.

Cleansing: Cleansers now come in many different forms: creams, wipes, washes, foams and soaps. You need to ensure that you use the correct cleanser for your skin type. Too strong a cleanser can leave your skin stripped of its natural defences, which exposes your skin to harmful irritants and allows vital moisture to escape. The whole point of using cleanser is to remove make-up and the day's build-up of grime so that your pores don't become blocked and prone to infection; if the cleanser is actually stripping away your skin's barrier, you are likely to end up with sensitive-skin flare-ups. If your skin feels tight after cleansing, your cleanser is probably too harsh.

Toning: Toners usually come in liquid form, and are designed to remove traces of cleanser while also tightening your pores. If you prefer, you could try a more natural alternative such as orange-flower water or rosewater.

Moisturizing: However good your skin may feel, please don't think it means you can skip this step. Contrary to common belief, moisturizers do not permeate the skin and moisturize from within. What they do is sit on the surface of the skin and prevent your skin's own moisture from escaping. Don't be fooled by pricey creams: they don't necessarily perform better the more expensive they are. You should try out cheaper brands, too; you will probably be pleasantly surprised by the results. Avoid moisturizers that leave your skin feeling greasy and opt for a matte finish instead – if nothing else, it's a far better base for make-up.

TOP 10 SKINCARE TIPS

1. **Take slow, deep breaths.** Oxygen helps to plump up and revitalize skin.
2. **Drink plenty of water.** It keeps dry skin at bay and helps you stay hydrated.
3. **Eat a balanced diet.** Your skin will benefit from all the required nutrients.
4. **Take regular exercise.** This keeps skin oxygenated and gives it that healthy glow.
5. **Avoid too much sun.** Excessive tanning is the fastest way to age your skin – enough said!
6. **Don't skip cleansing at the end of the day.** This keeps spots and blackheads away.
7. **Have plenty of sleep and rest.** There's a reason it's called 'beauty sleep' …
8. **Try the occasional facial steam.** This will keep your face hydrated, smooth and even.
9. **Eat plenty of fresh fruit and vegetables.** They are packed with vitamins and minerals.
10. **Quit smoking.** Smoke, like sun exposure, speeds up the ageing process.

3. What shape is your face?

In order to work out which hairstyles, glasses and make-up suit you best, it's a good idea to know what shape your face is. There are seven basic face shapes:

Oval: The length of your face is about one-and-a-half times the width, with high cheekbones and a gently curving jaw-line.

Round: You have a wide face with round cheeks and a rounded hairline and chin.

Square: You have a wide face with a straight hairline and an angular jaw.

Triangular/Pear: You have a narrow forehead and cheekbones and a wider chin.

Heart: Your face is narrow around the jaw but wider at the eyes.

Oblong: Your face is long and slender with a rounded hairline and jaw. Your forehead and cheeks are approximately the same width.

Diamond: Your forehead and jaw-line are narrow but you have wide cheekbones.

TOP TIP

If you're still a little stumped as to which category you fit into, try pushing all your hair back in an Alice band, then use an old lipstick to draw around your reflection in a mirror. Then step back and take a look; your face shape should be a lot clearer and easier to categorize.

4. Which hairstyles compliment your face?

OK, so now you know the shape of your face, it should be easier to determine which hairstyles will suit you. If this method of deduction all sounds a bit textbook to you – you're right, it is. There are some hairstyles that simply don't work well with certain face shapes. But with the following suggestions and some expert advice from your salon stylist, you'll be able to find your perfect glamorous hairstyle.

Oval: This is considered to be the ideal face shape, so count yourself lucky if this is you. You can get away with practically any hairstyle as your face is so versatile. You might, however, wish to avoid heavy styles or ones that partially cover or fall around your face, as you'll be hiding your great features. Instead, show off your perfection and opt for something that stays off your face – styles that you can push back, perhaps, or short crops.

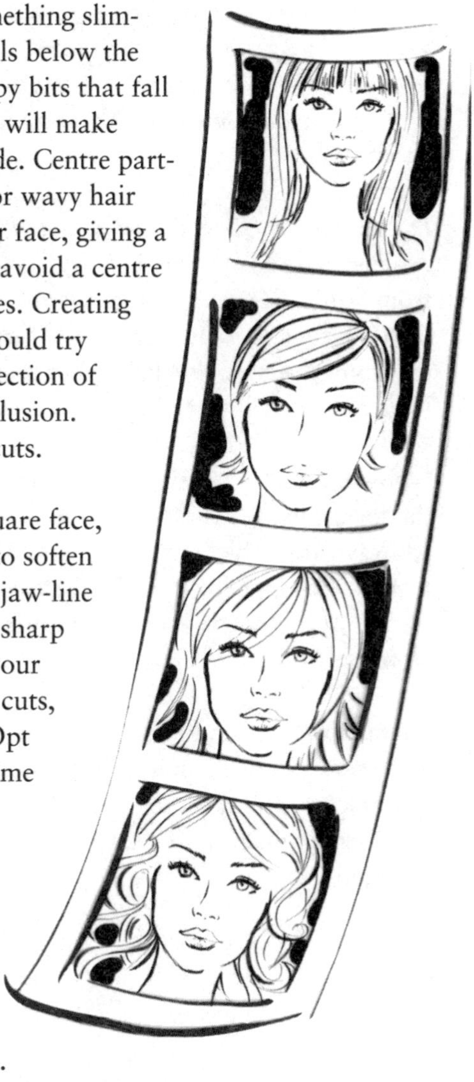

Round: If you have a round face, you may want to opt for something slimming. Try a style that falls below the chin, perhaps with choppy bits that fall onto your cheeks, which will make your face appear less wide. Centre partings with long, straight or wavy hair can help to elongate your face, giving a slimmer impression, but avoid a centre parting with shorter styles. Creating height also works; you could try backcombing the front section of your hair to create this illusion. Avoid one-length blunt cuts.

Square: If you have a square face, your hairstyle will need to soften the angles of either your jaw-line or your forehead. Avoid sharp cuts as they'll highlight your angles, as will geometric cuts, especially at chin level. Opt instead for styles that frame your face, maybe a long sweeping side fringe or a softly layered style that falls below the chin. Cascading waves or curls are good, but bear in mind they should be soft, not harsh.

Triangular/Pear: If you have a triangular face, your aim is likely to be narrowing the chin and widening the forehead. You can achieve this by opting for shorter cuts, which will balance your more prominent jaw-line. Textured crops work well, but avoid longer styles, as these will draw attention to your chin.

Heart: This is basically a reverse of the above. If you have a heart-shaped face, your aim will be to direct attention away from your wide temple and narrow chin. A heavy fringe will help to focus on your eyes, while a few strands of hair falling on your face may highlight your cheekbones. Chin-length or longer styles will work best.

Oblong: The key here is to try to add some width to the side of the face, so styles that give fullness would be good. You need to draw attention to your eyes and cheekbones. Peek-a-boo fringes are great for this, and soft curls or waves help to add width. Avoid centre partings with long hair, as this will only elongate your face.

Diamond: This is another great face shape, as most styles will suit you. Your aim may be to balance out your narrow or longer chin, so try either shoulder-length curls or chin-length bobs. Hair behind the ears also helps to highlight good cheekbones.

5. What make-up suits you best?

'Practice makes perfect' is a maxim that's true for most things in life, and make-up is no exception. Simply because we're women doesn't mean we're born with an innate expertise in buying and applying make-up; indeed, it can take years of experimentation to get it right. Some women feel that the more make-up they wear, the more attractive they become. Although they certainly draw attention to themselves, it's generally for the wrong reasons.

Wearing make-up is such an everyday event for most women, but it's amazing how many people get it wrong. There are three common make-up faux-pas:

1. **Wearing too much make-up.** You're aiming to look fabulous, not like Coco the Clown.

2. **Wearing the wrong style or colours.** This is as bad as wearing clothes that don't fit or suit you.

3. **Dodgy application.** There's really no point in wearing glamorous make-up if it looks as if you applied it during aeroplane turbulence.

If you take just a bit of time to avoid these make-up no-nos, it'll really make the difference between looking a total mess and looking naturally glamorous. The idea is to compliment and enhance your features and to look like a more polished version of yourself – not to slap on so many products that you render yourself unrecognizable. There are a few things to take into consideration when choosing your make-up ...

Skin tone: Your skin tone will broadly fit into one of two categories: warm or cool. Warm skin tones have yellow undertones and can be either olive, Mediterranean, Asian, dark or black skin types, usually with brown, green or hazel eyes. Cool skin tones have pink undertones: white skin types with blue or grey eyes.

Facial features: Facial features can play a big part in deciding which make-up you should wear most frequently. You may have thin lips that you want to enhance, or enchanting eyes you want to accentuate, or a nose you wish was a little smaller. There's more detail on how to do this in the next chapter.

Personal style: Your make-up should compliment the general style of your clothing and hair. If your style is contemporary or minimal, for instance, your make-up should reflect this; likewise, you wouldn't team a 1950s vintage dress with garish 1980s make-up. I hope.

Age: Although I'm not one to make a big deal of age, there are certain looks that might be best left to your teenage daughter. If you think your children, friends or husband might be mortified to see you dolled up like an 'Emo' kid, for example, that's probably not a great way to achieve glamorous mumhood!

FABULOUS FACE MASKS

Face masks are the ultimate luxury when it comes to pampering yourself, not least because they're such rare treats. But forget schlepping down to your local beautician with a car-full of kids; with these easy-to-make masks, you can lie back in the comfort of your own home and let Mother Nature work her magic.

Natural Glow

Planning a night out, but skin looks tired and drained? This will sort you out.

You will need:

1 guava
1 tablespoon oatmeal
A few drops of lemon juice

Mash the guava with a fork and then mix in the oatmeal and lemon juice. Apply to your face and neck, avoiding the eyes, and leave for 20 minutes. Rinse off to reveal instantly glowing skin.

A Carrot a Week

We all know that carrots are supposed to work wonders for our eyesight, but they can also perform miracles on tired skin.

You will need:

1 carrot
1 tablespoon honey

Grate the carrot and mix it with the honey. Apply to your face and neck and leave for 15 minutes, and then rinse off.

Repeat this once a week.

6. Which colours suit you?

Different colours bring out the best in different people. It all depends on the colour of your hair, eyes and skin as to which colours you can carry off. There are even 'colour consultants' who exist for the purpose of helping people understand which colours work for them. They help many individuals as well as large companies choose the best colours for attending interviews or concluding business deals, such is the importance of getting it right. It may sound ridiculous, but even on a smaller scale, wearing the right colour is a huge part of achieving an overall glamorous look.

Colour consultants can be pricey advisers, however, not to mention rather impersonal. Personally, I prefer the common-sense approach. Forget holding different colours up to your face, and instead hit shops with a stylish friend – someone you can trust to be brutally honest if you look awful. Failing that, you might book a personal stylist/shopper at a department store – this is a free service – and get some advice from someone in the know. When it comes to working out what suits you, you can't really beat trying on dozens of different combinations.

7. What style of dressing suits you?

Style is an achievable goal for everyone. Fashions come and go, and designer labels don't mean anything if you don't know how to wear them. Style is all about wearing fashions that look good on you – and having the confidence to know they make you look great.

Your dress code is obviously dependent on your daily life, and the social and professional scenarios to which you are exposed. Do you go out to work or are you a stay-at-home mum? Either way, there are a number of perils and pitfalls to negotiate.

WORKING MUM

It's easy to make less effort with your work outfits once you become a mum. Your priorities change, your time-management takes a knock – no more trying on five outfits every morning – and you barely have time to shop for new clothes, let alone experiment with your hair and make-up. Then there's the shoe dilemma: where you may have worn heels before, you now have to drop the kids off at school or nursery first, which can be a real schlep – so you resort to wearing comfortable trainers. So your already strangely-thrown-together outfit, which might have been saved by decent shoes, now looks positively ghastly.

STAY-AT-HOME MUM

Whether you had a day-job beforehand or not, it is very easy to fall into bad habits once you spend the majority of your day at home. Nevertheless, even if it's only at your book club or in the supermarket, presentation says an awful lot about your personality. So you need to set yourself some ground rules before you leave the house.

★ **No jogging bottoms.** Unless you are actually going jogging.

★ **No tatty or oversized jeans.** Jeans on the whole are fine, but make sure they don't look like hand-me-downs from your mother, or like the sort of jeans you'd wear for gardening.

★ **No stains.** This sounds painfully obvious – who would willingly wear dirty clothes? – but we've all had one of those mornings where our tops have ended up splattered in cereal or other baby-generated stains. Make sure you chuck the offending item into the washing basket and throw on something clean before going out.

IT'S ALL IN THE PLANNING

Get a weekly wardrobe routine up and running. Sort through your clothes and roughly plan your outfits for the week to coincide with your washing and ironing cycle, your meetings or lunchtime commitments, and any afternoons you may be expected to spend standing on a muddy sports field. Select a few basic pieces, a few dressy pieces and a few accessories to make your outfits more personal.

TOP TIP

You don't need to make every day a fashion parade, but you *do* need to look as though you have put some thought into your appearance. Trust me: you'll feel all the more glamorous and confident for it.

8. Which scents work well for you?

Fragrance is a subtle but important element of your general style. Wearing the perfect scent is like wearing matching underwear: it just feels right.

Putting perfume on sounds simple enough – you just point and spray, right? – but, as with colours and styles, some fragrances suit certain people and not others. Unlike colours and styles, however, wearing the right perfume is an actual science, since the same perfume can smell quite different depending on the wearer's chemical make-up. So, when choosing a scent, you should obviously go with the one whose smell you like best on yourself. The next chapter covers perfume-shopping in greater detail.

Ignore adverts and celebrity endorsements – it's no good smelling like Keira Knightley or Charlize Theron if the scent just isn't right for you – and just go for the one you like, whatever the brand.

9. What form of exercise benefits you most?

Deciding on an exercise regime is extremely important. You can't just pick any old exercise and hope it works wonders for your body; you have to pick the right exercise for you. Some people can diet and exercise for years without it making much of a visible difference, which can be really disheartening, to say the least.

There are two key things to take into consideration when working out which sort of exercise is most beneficial to your needs:

★ **Do you actually enjoy this particular form of exercise?** If you're going to do it properly and not make excuses as to why you can't possibly fit it in, it's vital that you look forward to the next session.

★ **Does your chosen form of exercise lead to visible results?** Do you feel fit and healthy after each session, and as if you've done something really good for your body?

If you're having trouble with either of these points, think about something you can incorporate into your daily routine. Walking is exercise in itself, and by ditching the car a few times a week will do you and your family the world of good. Dancing is another great form of exercise and, if you don't mind a few funny looks from the cat, can be done in your kitchen while cooking the dinner. Just stick on the radio or your favourite album and throw some shapes. The sillier you look, the more the kids will want to join in the fun, too.

10. Which healthy foods do you like?

Shockingly enough, there actually seem to be plenty of people out there who naturally gravitate away from the cookie jar and towards the fruit bowl. And unfortunately these people need to be emulated rather than ridiculed.

We could all do to take daily measures to ensure we eat the right amount of healthy food. And if carrots and Brussels sprouts are your sworn enemies: just think of all the behind-the-scenes work they'll be doing to make you look more healthy and glamorous.

We all think we know what a balanced diet is, even if we don't like to follow one, but let's just remind ourselves of the basics. After all, we are feeding hungry, impressionable kids who also need educating in this area, so it's a big responsibility.

THE FIVE BASIC FOOD GROUPS

A balanced diet incorporates elements of these five food groups, with the emphasis on the first three.

Carbohydrates: Otherwise known as starchy foods, carbs are where most of our energy and nutrients come from, and should therefore make up about one third of our diet. Without energy, it's impossible to do any exercise and stay trim. Carbs include potatoes, pasta, rice, bread and cereals.

VITAL VITAMINS

Our bodies require all kinds of vitamins and minerals in order to stay in top condition, and we don't always get what we're supposed to through our diets, no matter how healthy they may be. If you're vegetarian, for example, you may be lacking in iron; if you don't like kiwi or bananas, you could probably do to top up your potassium; if you can't tolerate milk and dairy products, you'll need a calcium supplement.

Each vitamin and mineral that is required by our body has a function or a task to perform, whether it's obvious to us or not. And since the condition of our skin, eyes, hair and nails all depends on the right vitamins and minerals, work out if there are any supplements you should be taking and think of them as a very quick and very easy beauty treatment.

A quick rundown of which of the main vitamins do what, and what you should be eating to make sure you get enough of them:

A: Found in carrots, tomatoes, sweet potato and apricots, vitamin A is beneficial to your eyes, lungs and skin.

B: The eight vitamins of the B-complex group are found in meat (especially liver and kidneys), green vegetables, nuts and grains, and they help to maintain a good metabolism.

C: Oranges and other citrus fruit, as well as spinach and broccoli, contain vital vitamin C, which helps strengthen bones and look after your skin.

D: While you can find vitamin D in oily fish products, it mainly comes from the sun. Its job is to help you absorb calcium, which is vital for strong teeth and bones.

E: Another key vitamin in terms of keeping your skin healthy and your cells in good condition, vitamin E is found in chicken, fish, vegetables, nuts and seeds.

K: Spinach, asparagus, Brussels sprouts and other dark leafy vegetables are a good source for this vitamin, which contributes to your body's ability to clot blood.

Fruit and vegetables: We've all heard nutritionists and even politicians banging on about 'five a day' and, unfortunately for some, they're quite right. Fruit and vegetables should make up about another third of our diet, with the Foods Standard Agency (FSA) recommending that we eat at least five portions daily. They are packed full of vitamins and minerals.

Proteins: Protein is a vital source of energy and vitamins, and can be found in foods such as meat, fish, eggs, beans and pulses. Proteins help repair cells during our beauty sleep, keeping us looking young and radiant.

Dairy: This group mainly consists of milk, cheese and yoghurts, all of which are important for our daily supply of calcium, which in turn is vital for strong, healthy bones. From a glamorous mum's point of view, calcium also contributes to healthy, shiny hair and strong nails.

Fat: Fat gets a bad rap, often for perfectly valid reasons. If you eat too much of it, it can be incredibly bad for you. The worst kinds of fat are saturated fats and those found in high-sugar foods (butter, cakes, pies, biscuits, pastry and cream), but there are also naturally occurring unsaturated fats in foods such as avocadoes, nuts and olive oil. 'Good fats' can help lower cholesterol and should have a small but nonetheless vital place in our diet.

TOP 3 HEALTHY-EATING TIPS

1. **Don't skip breakfast.** It really is the most beneficial meal of the day.
2. **Drink plenty of water to keep your digestion going.** Aim to drink at least two litres of water each day.
3. **Eat your five a day.** You're not getting up from the table until they're all gone!

Look the Part

In the last chapter, we did a thorough audit of our bodies, and should now have more of an idea of the elements that combine to make us look our most fabulous. This chapter is all about details: how to apply your chosen make-up, sort out your skin and generally transform your beauty regime for the better.

LESS IS MORE

First off, let's get back to basics and understand a little bit about what we are actually trying to achieve. Do you think of make-up as:

a) a way to enhance your best assets
 or
b) a mask?

If your answer is more b) than a), you need to work on your self-perception before being let loose with the foundation. Unless you're starring on Broadway, make-up is an enhancement rather than a disguise, and ought to be applied subtly, not with a trowel.

Make-up junkies tend to make one rather big mistake and that is to try to accentuate every area of their face – huge eyes, huge lips, rosy cheeks – and the result is often rather alarming. When it comes to make-up application, one of the first lessons to come to terms with is that less is actually more. Your focus should be on one area alone; if you have lovely eyes that you'd like to emphasize, keep your lips and cheeks toned down. If, on the other hand, you want to wear really bold lips, don't go mad with the eye shadow.

Whatever your facial hang-ups may be, carefully chosen and cleverly applied make-up can enhance, accentuate, reduce, divert attention from, and draw attention to whichever features you wish.

FACE PREP

Before we get started on the more exciting products, there are some simple steps you can follow in order to ensure your face is ready to be worked on.

1. Start with a clean, moisturized face, and clean hands. Moisturizer, as well as doing what it says on the tin, also acts as a great base for make-up, helping it to stay put for longer, so make sure you moisturize well.

2. Eye cream can also work wonders, especially as we get older. Apply it very sparingly, literally just beneath the eye. It'll act as a great base for under-eye concealer, should you need it.

3. If you have very dark circles under your eyes, you may need to use a corrector stick before using the concealer. To help lighten dark circles, use a brush to apply your concealer to the area beneath your lower lash, and then use your fingers to pat it until it blends in. Some people apply concealer before foundation, while others do it afterwards. It really doesn't matter which you prefer.

10-STEP BEAUTY TREATMENT

1. Get to first base

Foundation performs a simple job but it's so very easy to get it wrong. If you've worn foundation before, as most women have, you'll know just how difficult it is to find that perfect shade – and when you do find it, you just pray that the cosmetic company doesn't decide to discontinue it tomorrow. It's almost worth buying it in bulk.

There is a bewildering array of different foundations out there these days, which is as much a blessing as a curse. Where to begin? The good news, however, is that modern formulations are much more subtle than foundations of yore, and as a result it's becoming ever more tricky to spot whether someone is wearing foundation or not. This can only be a good thing.

DO I ACTUALLY NEED TO WEAR FOUNDATION?

Even if you've worn foundation since your teenage years, stop for a moment to think whether you actually need to wear it.

What does foundation actually do? Well, its primary job is to camouflage any skin imperfections you might have, to even out skin tone and make your skin appear more flawless. If your skin already looks pretty smooth in comparison to most other people's, you could be one of the lucky few who can bypass this stage altogether. Congratulations!

If, however, you think your skin could benefit from a touch of help, the following tips should help you find the right foundation for you.

★ Go shopping without make-up on and in daylight, equipped with cotton buds, a compact mirror, face wipes, an open mind and lots of determination.

★ Test three or four relevant shades at a time, drawing vertical stripes down your face, from just under your cheekbone to your jaw. If you need to go outside to get a decent view in natural light, do so – you're equipped with your own mirror – but for goodness' sake don't wander out of the store carrying four tubes of foundation.

★ If one of the stripes disappears into your skin, you've hit the jackpot. If not, use your wipes and try again.

★ Don't be afraid to test different types of foundation: liquids, mousses, sticks or good old compacts.

Once you've whittled it down to the perfect foundation for your skin tone, there are a few more pointers in terms of getting the stuff onto your face.

★ Don't think that you need more foundation the older you get. Foundation can in fact look particularly bad on lines and creases, so limit your use of it to spots and blemishes.

★ If you have the time, let your moisturizer settle on your face for five or ten minutes before you apply your foundation.

★ There are various ways in which you can apply your foundation, and the choice is yours. You can use a sponge, a brush or, as many make-up artists do, the tips of your *clean* fingers.

★ Don't stand too close to the mirror, and certainly don't use a magnifying mirror – as this will turn your pores into potholes and any imperfections into mole hills, and you'll end up needing a shovel to hide all of that. Use as little as possible, remembering that the whole point of foundation is to smooth away imperfections and even out skin tone without burying your natural complexion. Remember: you are not icing a cake.

★ Tinted moisturizers are a brilliant solution if your skin is basically fine but you'd like a little assistance. As with foundation, tinted moisturizers come in multiple shades and should be tested in the same way. The coverage is much lighter, which makes them perfect for younger skin or when you're having a 'good skin day'.

FIVE FOR THE FACE

Our faces gradually lose their elasticity as the years go by, but a regular facial workout can really slow the process down. Ignore all those TV ads that tell you facial surgery is the latest must-have procedure and try these exercises out instead.

On the Chin

1. Jut out your jaw, open your mouth wide and pull your bottom lip over your bottom teeth. Then move your jaw up and down – you'll look like a cartoon robot but stick with it. Repeat this ten times, twice a day – although preferably in the privacy of your own home …
2. Sit in a relaxed position. Tilt your head upwards and purse your lips. Hold for five seconds and then relax. Repeat ten times.
3. Start with your teeth together, and then open your jaw very slightly. Move your lower jaw slowly to one side, as far as it will go, and then return slowly to the centre position. Repeat this ten times and then work the other side.

Eye Eye

4. Close your eyes and lift your eyebrows as high up as you can, as though very surprised. Hold the position for five seconds and then relax. Repeat this ten times.

Cheeky

5. Sit upright, facing forwards with your lips closed but relaxed. Pucker and pout your lips using your cheek muscles, hold the position for ten seconds, and then relax. Repeat this ten times.

2. Be cheeky

I always regard blusher as the fun side of make-up. Foundation and concealer are serious, and have serious jobs to do around the face, in contrast to which blusher seems flippant, flirty and cheeky. As with all make-up, there are a couple of rules when it comes to blusher, since the colour you choose needs to compliment your skin tone, but on the whole you can go for as bright or dull a shade as you like – within reason.

Strictly speaking:

- ★ Ivory skin tones should opt for light beige tones
- ★ Pink skin tones should opt for peachy tones
- ★ Yellow skin tones should opt for honey or peachy coral tones
- ★ Black skin tones should opt for toffee or bronze tones

The traditional purpose of using blusher is to look as though you've been for a brisk walk in the country – a natural flush to the cheeks – and not as though you're auditioning for *Madame Butterfly*. Test a few different shades on your cheeks or on the back of your hand while out shopping, and take the time to decide whether the right blusher for you comes as a cream, stain, gel, powder or bronzer.

Application should be to the apples of your cheeks (where you blush) and not all along the cheekbone as some people evidently think. If you're not sure of the exact area, smile into a mirror – the apples of your cheeks will rise upwards. Once you've applied it to this area, it's fine to continue a little way along the cheekbone outwards towards your hairline.

TOP TIP

Unless you are super-confident, take care when applying stains. They look great when applied correctly and last for ages, but they dry really rapidly after application, leaving very little blend-time. If you're not fast enough, you will resemble Aunt Sally, which is unlikely to be the look you were hoping for.

3. Use your eyes

When it comes to applying make-up to your eyes, there are four main areas for consideration: eye shadow, eyeliner, mascara and eyebrows.

EYE SHADOW

If you don't have bags of time in the morning, opting for a neutral shade is a wise choice, not least because neutral shades don't require so much blending. Save the more risqué shades for the evenings. Often, the most striking shades of eye shadow are those that contrast with your eyes; so, for instance, you might wear brown eye shadow if you have green eyes. But the best thing is to experiment. Go out and buy a few cheap eye shadows in colours you like and which you know you'd feel confident enough to wear. Then test them at home, mixing colours if you want to create your own shade. When you've got the shade right, you can go out and invest in a more expensive product, safe in the knowledge that it'll suit you. Make-up consultants at beauty counters will be able to help you find the right shade if you show them the sort of thing you're after.

EYELINER

For some people eyeliner is an absolute necessity and they feel naked without it. You can wear it above or below the eye, or of course both – it's entirely up to you. If you have narrow or small eyes, wearing eyeliner on your bottom lids can help open the eyes up and give them a larger appearance. Eyeliner comes in various forms – including powder-based pencil, kohl pencil and liquid liner – and many make-up artists even advise older women to apply a spot of eye shadow to the area instead, to avoid too severe a look.

TOP 5 EYELINER APPLICATION TIPS

1. Kohl pencils are much softer than powder- or wax-based pencils and are therefore gentler on the eye, but always make sure they're nicely sharpened.
2. Work as close to the lashes as possible: just above the lash on the top lid, and either above or below the lash on the bottom lid.
3. Don't feel you have to draw a continuous line around the eye. A short line at the top and bottom is fine if that's what you prefer.
4. On the lower lid, start from the outer edge and work inwards. On the top lid, start in the middle and work outwards, and then go back to the inside corner and work your way to the middle.
5. Unlike when you apply foundation, it's a good idea to use a magnifying mirror for this – it'll make it a whole lot easier.

MASCARA

Most people choose black mascara as a matter of course, but there are all kinds of colours out there. The lighter ones work best on redheads, blondes and those after a more natural look. Price is not necessarily indicative of quality, so don't feel embarrassed if your favourite brand is in fact the cheapest.

Whichever colour you choose, these pointers may help you make the most of your dazzling eyes.

★ Use an eyelash curler before applying mascara if you want to make your lashes more dynamic.

★ Start applying mascara from the underside of your lashes, beginning at the base and brushing towards the tip, curling the lashes as you go.

★ Twist and wiggle the wand as you move along the lashes, as this will help to cover each individual lash separately.

★ Only apply mascara to your top lashes if your intention is to open up the eye.

★ If your application is a bit dodgy and you end up with 'spider lashes', don't try to fix the problem by applying more mascara to the wand and using it to separate the lashes – you'll only end up compounding the mess by applying far too much mascara. It's far better to remove what you've done using eye make-up remover and then start again.

TOP TIP

Replace your mascara every three to six months, for the sake of hygiene as well as to avoid ending up with a bottle of dry gloop.

EYEBROWS

Eyebrows can be a beauty nightmare, whether you pluck them or not. They seem determined to spread in all directions, becoming bushy when left unattended and spiky when over-plucked. If you have stray brows, keep them in check with a pair of slanted tweezers – but please, please, *please* don't get carried away. We've all heard nightmare stories about a friend of a friend who plucked them over-zealously and they never grew back! Eyebrows are strange creatures and you never know what they might do next ...

TOP 3 EYEBROW TIPS

1. Eyebrow guru Shavata recommends plucking from underneath and leaving the top untouched, so as not to ruin your brows' natural shape or end up with a prickly mess encroaching on your forehead.
2. Tame unruly brows using petroleum jelly or clear mascara. If they are particularly naughty, invest in a special brow brush (a bit like a toothbrush) and some brow gel – that'll keep them in line!
3. If you want to give the illusion that you have thick, shapely brows, use a brow pencil in upward diagonal strokes, following the shape of the arch. Obviously use a shade similar to that of your brows.

4. Get lippy

There was a time when there was only one option for lips: lipstick. Now we have glosses, stains, sheer sticks, lip-plumpers, long lasting colours, lip shimmers and tinted balms to contend with. Don't get me wrong, choice is good and I'm all for it, but there are just so many more products to spend your money on these days that it's hard to know where to begin.

So really it's all down to personal preference as to which one you choose. Lip gloss is very much 'in' at the moment, and it's certainly much easier to deal with than the other options, requiring minimum effort and no real artistry, let alone a mirror. Gone are the days when it really was necessary to go to the powder room to re-apply.

The basic lipstick colour rules are:

★ Light skin tones: light browns/oranges and pinks

★ Medium skin tones: brownish reds and light browns

★ Dark skin tones: plums and deep reds

The colour rules are fairly hypothetical these days, though, since the vast array of lip products makes it easier for you to wear shades you would once have considered impossible. So if you thought you couldn't wear red lipstick because your skin tone was too pale, think again: perhaps try a red sheer tint or gloss for a slightly subtler look.

If you think your lips are too thin, glosses and shimmers can give the illusion of fuller lips, although a lot of women opt for the newer lip-plumpers. These do tend to have a noticeable effect, although they often make your lips tingle as though you've eaten a chili pepper. Still, it's worth it if you're paranoid about thin lips.

Remember: if you're into dramatic eye make-up, stay away from strong colour on your lips, opting instead for something natural or neutral, and vice versa. If you like wearing bold colour on your lips, go easy on the eyes and the blusher.

Here are some more lipstick application tips:

- ★ First, apply some balm or petroleum jelly to keep lips moist. Using a lip liner, begin at the V ('Cupid's bow') on your top lip and draw outwards to either side. Then do the same on your bottom lip. Line the very outer edge to give the impression of fuller lips, or inside the edge if you want to reduce your lips' appearance. For a lasting finish, use the liner all over your lips, so that a hint of colour remains once the lipstick fades.
- ★ For a really polished look, use a lip brush to apply the lipstick. Not only will you use less lipstick this way, but it'll also stay on longer and give more of a perfect Hollywood effect.
- ★ Apply a first coat of lipstick and then blot your lips with a tissue before applying a second coat. This might sound old-fashioned, but make-up artists still use this method as it helps to ensure a more lasting finish.

TOP TIP

For soft, smooth lips, buff them every few days with a soft toothbrush to remove flaky skin, and then apply lip balm. Before bed you can either moisturize your lips with your regular moisturizer or else a generous application of lip balm.

5. Have the upper hand

Dry hands and chipped nails tend to come with the mums' territory. So what can we do? There may be no escaping the tasks that wreak havoc on our hands – bathing the kids, washing and peeling the veg – but there are ways in which you can minimize the damage to your hands and nails. A few small steps can help make a big difference.

★ Leave hand cream strategically positioned around the house. By the kitchen sink, by the bathroom sink, by your bed and one in your handbag for when you're out and about. Get into the habit of using it frequently throughout the day.

★ Use a hand scrub or exfoliator once a week. This will help to banish the rough, dry skin and keep your hands smooth.

★ Always wear gloves for washing up and gardening, and of course in cold weather.

★ Where possible use gentle hand wipes rather than water. Ironically, an excess of water can actually make your hands drier.

★ Give your hands some extra-special TLC when you've been doing something repetitive such as peeling potatoes, digging in the garden or using weights machines at the gym. You may not be able to see it straight away, but these sorts of activities can leave you with rough skin or calluses later on in the evening; the sooner you can apply some intensive moisturizer, the better.

NAIL IT

It's all very well looking after your hands, but if your nails look awful it's almost a wasted effort. For mums who don't have time to visit a nail bar – and let's face it, that's most of us – here are two five-minute wonder manicures:

Manicure 1

1. For uneven nails, use a nail file from side to centre to even them up.

2. Take a good old-fashioned white nail pencil, and run it along the underside of the edge of the nail. This is a very speedy but effective version of the French manicure.

3. Finally, put a tiny dot of cuticle oil on each nail, rub it in and then buff. Perfect.

Manicure 2

1. File nails as in Manicure 1.

2. Choose a quick-drying pale or neutral shade of varnish (any mistakes you make, assuming you're in a hurry, will be less obvious) and apply one coat.

3. Use a quick-drying top coat or a blast of cold air from a hairdryer, and you're done.

TOP 5 NAIL TIPS

1. Keep some cuticle oil by your bed, so that you can massage some into your hands and cuticles when you apply hand cream at night.
2. Use acetone-free nail varnish remover on brittle nails, as it's gentler and less drying.
3. If you treat yourself to a salon manicure, take your favourite polish with you and ask the beautician to use that. This way, you can make any necessary touch-ups at home, thereby extending the manicure's life.
4. File your nails in such a way that they resemble the nail base, as this looks neater and more professional. Most women opt for the 'squoval' – a square with smoothed oval edges – but if you have a square nail base, go for a square finish.
5. Get into the habit of removing chipped polish – going varnish-free is far more presentable than the chipped look.

6. Feel footloose and fancy-free

What could be worse than getting glammed up for a special occasion, and then looking down to see ghastly feet? Well, OK, plenty could be worse – but from a glamorous perspective, it's pretty bad.

Traditionally, women start to panic about the state of their feet at the beginning of the annual wedding season, when strappy sandals become compulsory. Hastily applying some colourful nail polish in the car en route to the ceremony, we can't help but think, 'I hope nobody looks at my feet – I must sort them out before the next wedding ...'

Unfortunately, having healthy-looking feet takes both time and effort – after all, we can't have our feet wrapped up in boots for three-quarters of the year and then expect, come summer, that they will be as flip-flop-ready as we are.

Our feet, like our hands, take a real bashing on a daily basis. They are one of the hardest-working parts of our bodies and yet we pay little or no attention to them. The good news is that you don't need to splash out on salon pedicures to get them on the straight and narrow. Try this at-home pedicure once a fortnight and you should see a dramatic improvement.

TOP TIP

When it's not too muggy, apply your nightly foot cream (or body moisturizer) to clean feet and then sleep with your socks on. Your feet should feel silky smooth by morning.

PERFECT PEDICURE

★ Fill a basin with warm water and add a few drops of peppermint essential oil – feet love to be revived with this – or else any other foot-soak product you've no doubt received for Christmas.

★ Soak your feet (nails should be free of polish) for at least five minutes, ten if you have the time.

★ Pat your feet dry with a towel.

★ Use a foot file to remove (gently) any dead, flaky or rough skin.

★ Use a pair of nail scissors or clippers to cut your nails straight across. Take care not to cut them too short, otherwise you run the risk of in-growing toenails. Gently file any rough edges.

★ Soak and dry your feet again if you have time. If not, brush them off and move on to the next stage.

★ Give yourself a foot massage with a good, thick foot cream (or rich moisturizer).

★ Apply some nail varnish remover to a cotton pad and use this to wipe any moisturizer off your toenails, in preparation for the varnish.

★ If you're short on time and can't afford to make mistakes, opt for a lighter shade of varnish, so that any mistakes aren't too obvious. If you're keen on a darker shade, arm yourself with a cotton bud doused in nail varnish remover.

7. Don't get caught by the fuzz

Where personal appearance is concerned, there are few things more liberating than the feeling of freshly shaved or waxed legs. There's something so satisfying about moisturizing stubble-free legs, not to mention the wardrobe opportunities that suddenly reopen. Be gone, opaque tights and jeans in the height of summer!

So let's run through our options for underarms, legs, bikini line, and – dare I mention it – facial hair of any description. There are quite a few different methods for getting rid of unwanted hair, and the one you choose will depend on a number of variables:

★ How much hair do you need to remove?

★ How often do you need to remove it?

★ Which part of your body are you treating?

★ How much time and privacy do you have?

★ How much are you prepared to spend?

BLEACHING

HOW IT WORKS: Well, as the name suggests, it's not hair removal at all – it disguises the hair by temporarily lightening it

HOW LONG DOES IT LAST? Anywhere between two and four weeks

COST: Only costs a few pounds in salons, while home kits are readily available and reasonably priced

PROS: It's a cheap and effective method for some

CONS: Some people suffer allergic reactions to the chemicals – always do a patch test before slathering on too much – and it's also not very good at disguising thicker patches of unwanted hair

IDEAL FOR: Facial hair

NEVER USE ON: Sensitive skin

DEPILATORY CREAM

HOW IT WORKS: Chemicals dissolve the hair on the skin's surface

HOW LONG DOES IT LAST? Anywhere from a few days to a week

COST: Relatively cheap compared to other methods

PROS: Very quick and easy to use in the comfort of your own bathroom

CONS: Some people suffer allergic reactions to the chemicals – always do a patch test

IDEAL FOR: Longer hair rather than stubble

NEVER USE ON: Sensitive skin

ELECTROLYSIS

HOW IT WORKS: A fine needle is inserted into the hair follicle and tiny electrical currents are passed through it, killing the root

HOW LONG DOES IT LAST? It can be permanent, after several sessions

COST: Can be costly as you have to repeat the procedure over a few months, but worth it if you really want to be hair-free for good

PROS: The effects are often permanent if you persist with the treatment

CONS: Each hair is worked on individually, so it may take quite a few visits. Skin redness and swelling can occur for a few hours after treatment

IDEAL FOR: Most body areas

NEVER USE ON: The bikini line, if you can help it – it can be really painful

EPILATOR

HOW IT WORKS: A handheld electrical device pulls multiple hairs out from the root

HOW LONG DOES IT LAST? Up to three or four weeks

COST: The initial cost of an epilator – which is probably just a little more than the cost of one leg-and-bikini wax at a salon

PROS: Easy enough to do yourself at home

CONS: Can be a bit painful, leaving a little redness for a couple of hours, and you do run the risk of ingrown hairs

IDEAL FOR: Arms and legs

NEVER USE ON: Sensitive areas

LASER

HOW IT WORKS: Laser deactivates the hair follicles, causing the hair to fall out

HOW LONG DOES IT LAST? It can be permanent, after several sessions

COST: Expensive. Worth saving up for if it'll make a noticeable difference to you, though

PROS: The effects are often permanent

CONS: Can be very effective for light-skinned, dark-haired girls, but not great for other skin/hair combinations as the laser can have trouble differentiating between skin and hair

IDEAL FOR: Facial hair

NEVER USE ON: Eyebrows or lashes, due to proximity to eyes

SHAVING

HOW IT WORKS: A razor cuts the hair off at the skin's surface

HOW LONG DOES IT LAST? From one day to half a week

COST: Cheap as chips

PROS: It's very cheap and can be done at home in the shower

CONS: Hair will feel bristly as it grows back. Doesn't last very long and hair may grow back thicker and darker.

IDEAL FOR: Legs and underarms

NEVER USE ON: Facial hair, as you run the risk of stubble

WAXING

HOW IT WORKS: Warm wax is applied to the hair, followed by strips of cloth or paper. The wax and hair stick to the paper, which is quickly stripped off (against the direction of the hair's growth) to leave you hair-free

HOW LONG DOES IT LAST? Anywhere between two and six weeks, since hair is ripped out at the root

COST: Prices vary from salon to salon. While some are quite reasonable, others are ridiculous, so shop around. Waxing kits can be bought for home use at very reasonable prices, although the quality of the results will depend on your nerves and pain threshold...

PROS: Leaves skin silky-smooth and hair-free for up to six weeks. If you wax your hair regularly, the rate of re-growth will slow and the hair should become softer over time.

CONS: Can be a tad painful and you may get the odd in-grown hairs

IDEAL FOR: Most body areas, including the upper lip

NEVER USE ON: Sensitive skin

8. Love the skin you're in

Exercise and diet aside, we can all give our appearance a bit of a boost by paying attention to our skin. We're all guilty of envying other people's smooth arms or blemish-free faces, but there are lots of small ways in which we can make the most of the skin we are, for better or worse, stuck with.

If your skin looks a bit dull and tired, these suggestions may help give it a glowing radiance that's red-carpet-worthy (or simply school-gate-worthy).

★ **Use a body scrub at least once a week.** Get yourself a scrub that's suited to your skin type. They come in a wide range of varieties – and with wildly differing prices – from the supermarket budget versions to the swankier brands. Ignore the label and go for the one that has the best effect on your skin.

★ **Use an exfoliating shower gel daily.** These are gentle on the skin and perfect for everyday use. Squeeze out a small amount and massage it in, starting from your feet and working your way up your body, in circular motions towards the heart. Rinse off carefully, using a loofah or body glove.

WATER, WATER EVERYWHERE

Scientific types recommend we drink two litres of water per day. It sounds an awful lot but if you consider that good hydration is what keeps us alert and energetic, it really is worth struggling through. Personally, adhering to the two-litres-a-day rule made me realize that a) I had previously been suffering from dry skin; and b) headaches did not have to form an integral part of my daily routine. Dehydration is an instant way to dull the look of your hair, skin and eyes, and can really put a dampener on your glamorous efforts, not least by giving you a crashing headache when you're supposed to be feeling fabulous.

If you think you'll find it difficult to get through two litres each day, fill a 500ml bottle with water and set yourself the challenge of refilling it four times during the day. You could carry a small bottle of water around in your handbag, and get used to having a swig every now and then. Tea, coffee, alcohol and caffeinated soft drinks are not to be included in your daily water intake, more's the pity, as they tend to have the reverse effect and leave you more dehydrated than before.

An easy way to get your day off to a hydrated start is to substitute your morning coffee with a cup of warm water with lemon juice. This aids your general digestion, helps flush out toxins in the liver, and frankly tastes a bit more interesting than boring old water. What's more, it makes you feel virtuous at the same time, so is a win-win tactic as far as fabulousness is concerned.

★ **Use plenty of moisturizer.** With all those dead, flaky skin cells washed away, your skin will be tingling and refreshed, but very much in need of some soothing cream.

Keep these easy things up throughout the year and you'll soon see a noticeable difference in your skin. If you're a fake-tan fan, you'll also find it much easier to achieve that post-holiday look, since your smoother and more even skin will be more receptive to bronzing lotions.

TOP TIP

If you fancy trying out the sun-kissed look but aren't into fake tan, try a shimmer body lotion or a lotion with gradual tanning ingredients. Both achieve a warm glow without turning you orange.

9. Polish your pearly whites

As we remind the kids so often, brushing our teeth every morning and evening is a minimum requirement when it comes to having a gorgeous smile. If, however, you're serious about improving the state of your teeth, brushing after each meal is more the order of the day, as is regular rinsing with mouthwash, and increasing your intake of both calcium and water.

PEARLY WHITES: 5 THINGS TO ENJOY IN ABUNDANCE

1. Broccoli
2. Spinach
3. Celery
4. Carrots
5. Milk

PEARLY WHITES: 5 THINGS TO AVOID LIKE THE PLAGUE (WITHIN REASON)

1. Red wine
2. Caffeine
3. Fizzy drinks
4. Acidic drinks such as fruit juice
5. Smoking

Another great reason to cut down on these tooth-staining temptations is that many of them also contribute to bad breath – which I probably don't need to point out is not terribly glamorous. If you're worried about breath freshness, there are a few things you can do to minimize your susceptibility:

★ **Spurn smelly food.** Avoid eating anything with a strong smell for a few hours before meeting other people. We all know that onions and garlic will linger for a surprisingly long time, but strong cheeses, distinctive spices (such as cumin) and coffee can all develop into unpleasant odours on your breath.

★ **Shun sugars.** Sugar is quickly and easily converted by bacteria into breath-souring acid. This goes for the sugars you find in sweets as well as in sugary drinks from cola to beer. Drink sugar-free alternatives where possible, or stick to water.

★ **Don't have a dry mouth.** Bad breath bacteria love a dry mouth – as we all know from the horror that is 'morning breath' – so keep a small bottle of water in your handbag to top up your fluid levels throughout the day. A few gulps will flush away the bacteria or seriously dilute their potency, leaving you fantastically fresh-breathed.

★ **Brush, floss, swill.** Maintain good oral hygiene by brushing and flossing regularly and by using a mouthwash with as little alcohol content as possible, since alcohol dries the mouth.

★ **Crunch crudités.** Snacking on carrots, celery, radishes, cucumber and apples can have a natural tooth-cleaning effect, as the crunchy texture rubs against your teeth rather than sticking to them.

★ **Chew gum.** Sugarless gum, to be precise. It increases saliva production, which in turn fights the acids caused by bad breath bacteria. You could also try chewing parsley or mint leaves, but gum is rather more handbag-friendly.

TOP TIP

Orange-tone lipsticks really bring out the yellow in teeth, as do stark white shirts and gold jewellery. If you're worried about the colour of your teeth, you can minimize their effect by wearing off-white or cream clothing and silver jewellery, while bronzer and darker shades of lipstick can work wonders.

10. Be simply scent-sational

Once you've gone through your showering and make-up rituals, a spritz of your favourite scent really is the icing on the cake. You probably have a favourite perfume, but there's no reason why you shouldn't wear a different scent for different occasions – after all, the perfect perfume for a romantic date may not be your scent of choice on parents' evening.

NOTES ON PERFUME

Every perfume is a product of three fairly distinct levels – or 'notes', to use the technical term.

Top notes: These are the first scents you will smell when you spray the perfume. The top notes are the perfume's signature smell and tend to be very distinctive, if not overwhelming.

Mid notes: These emerge once the elements that make up the top notes begin to evaporate. The mid notes are a pleasant middle-ground between the overpowering top notes and the long-lasting base notes.

Base notes: Once you've worn a perfume for about half an hour, the base notes are the scent that remains, and which essentially form the lasting scent of any perfume.

Buying perfume is a deceptively simple prospect: go to a shop, smell a few things, buy the one you like best, right? But if you've ever found yourself standing baffled in front of an array of alluring bottles, so overpowered by fragrance that you've lost your sense of smell, you'll know that it's not as easy a task at it sounds. Here are a few tips for your next perfume-shopping experience.

★ Go as early in the day as is possible, so the department stores are quiet and calm, and the air isn't already full of conflicting scents.

★ Wear fresh clothes to avoid existing perfume smells.

★ Don't test too many scents in any one shopping trip – after overwhelming your nose with the strong top notes of three or four perfumes, you will effectively lose your sense of smell.

★ Test perfumes using the blotting sticks rather than spraying them onto your skin, and whittle down your choices to two scents.

★ Spray one scent on each wrist (the crease of your elbow works well, too), and then take yourself off for a half-hour wander around some other shops, to let the base notes develop and to give your nose a break.

★ Ask for a sample if you're not entirely convinced about your choice. This way you can wear it at home for a few days and – something rather important – make sure your partner and children don't find the scent repellent.

TOP TIP

Don't rush out to buy a perfume you love on somebody else without testing it on your own skin first. When you enjoy the scent of someone's perfume, what you in fact smell is the combination of the perfume's base notes on that specific person's skin – it's almost a unique scent.

Dress to Impress

Gorgeous make-up: check. Smooth legs: check. Radiant skin, lustrous hair, elegant nails: check, check, check. OK, we're ready to move on to personal style.

Whether we like it or not, our clothes say an awful lot about us. They are, after all, the first thing we notice when we pass other people in the street or sit opposite them in meetings, and we're all guilty of making character judgments about complete strangers based entirely on the combination of clothes they picked out that morning.

FASHION RULES

Whether you're planning on sorting the wheat from the chaff in your wardrobe or preparing for a complete style overhaul, there are three basic things to bear in mind:

1. **Quality:** An untidy hem or cheap fabric can really let an otherwise gorgeous item of clothing down. Think of all the things that would lead you to assume an item was badly made, and avoid them. The good news is that clothes don't need to be expensive in order to look as if they're of a decent quality.

2. **Price:** Nor indeed do they need to be expensive full-stop. Designer clothes are not always superior to cheaper options, and they certainly won't do anything for your bank balance. High-street stores are getting very canny these days when it comes to imitating the latest designer styles, so look in magazines and shop around for designer-inspired fashion at a snip of the price.

3. **Fashion:** You don't have to be Anna Wintour to know when an item of clothing is entirely unfashionable. Mums aren't traditionally renowned for their on-trend fashion sense, and there's absolutely no need to follow fashions slavishly, but do avoid items that went out of fashion for a reason. A huge part of being glamorous is giving off the right impression, which unfortunately you will not do if you wear shellsuits, tassels, leopard-print or any other fashion disasters best confined to history.

10-STEP GUIDE TO A WONDERFUL WARDROBE

1. What's your style?

The key to looking stylish is not just buying the latest fashions and splashing out on expensive heels; it's all about knowing what looks good on you and pulling it off with confidence and panache. If what looks particularly good on you is a stylish pair of jeans and a crisp white shirt with a simple pair of ballet pumps and some colourful accessories, so be it.

Have you created a style of your own or are you a dedicated follower of fashion? Both are of course fine, if they're done well. The problem with following fashions as we become more life-experienced (OK, older) is that we run the risk of looking like mutton dressed as lamb. If a new fashion comes along that you don't think will do justice to your features, or which will embarrass your teenage daughter at parents' evening, give it a miss and wait for something more flattering to become fashionable. Knowing what will *not* suit you is just as important as knowing what will. While some enviable people can pull off the same wonderful style for decades on end – I'm thinking Jackie Kennedy, Audrey Hepburn and their ilk – others need to change and adapt as they get older.

If you really do despair of the state of your wardrobe and have no idea whether you want a look that's smart, casual, trendy, classic, sporty, retro, bohemian or some sort of hybrid, there are some easy and even quite fun ways of whittling down your options:

★ Buy a few women's mags and tear out pages on which you see something you like, even if it's just a belt or a style of earring. By the end of the exercise you should have a clearer idea of the sorts of things that stand out for you.

★ Go window-shopping and make a note of styles you like. If you come across a department store with a range of items that catch your eye, book yourself an appointment with their personal shopper.

★ Take your best friend out shopping with you. She will probably prove more useful than a personal shopper, since she knows your personality better than anyone and won't encourage you to buy things that don't look 100 per cent fabulous.

TOP TIP

If you're still a bit stuck, try on anything and everything until you find a few key shapes that work for you. It doesn't matter whether you prefer trousers to dresses and skirts or vice versa; the job in hand is to pick something you feel comfortable enough to wear, and which compliments your body shape and other features.

2. Which colours suit you?

If you're colour-shy or just don't know which colours work for you, put your best friend or personal shopper to further use in helping you select some splashes of colour. Everyone loves a bit of black – it's so classic, so flattering – but too much black can look like a disguise rather than a fashion statement, and it's good to mix things up a bit every now and then. And I don't just mean switch to navy or dark brown! (Both, incidentally, as elegant and flattering as black for most shapes and sizes.)

But back to colour. Make the most of your shopping trip, especially if you have someone in tow to help you, by trying on colours you may not usually have considered. A quick trick if you find yourself short on time and overwhelmed with possibilities is to hold a garment up to your face – if it makes your complexion look pale and dull, the colour isn't for you. If it adds radiance to your face, try the thing on pronto.

The brightest colours will always look great on dark-skinned and tanned women, while pale colours can work wonders for those with alabaster skin. But there really are no strict rules when it comes to colour – see how adventurous you dare to be.

TOP TIP

If your intensive trying-on sessions really don't yield a colour or pattern you feel comfortable with, introduce some splashes of colour using accessories: jewellery, belts, scarves, handbags, hats and even shoes. They'll make all the difference to your overall look without involving too much of a departure from the comforts of black and brown.

FIX A FASHION DILEMMA

Oooops! Matching outfits

Turning up at the school gates in your most fabulous outfit only to find a rival mum wearing the same thing ranks very highly on the glamorous-mum disaster scale. What to do?

1. Avoid wearing new-to-the-high-street distinctive outfits, since your rivals will probably have been to the same shops. Keep these outfits for occasions where you're less likely to run into quite so many time-strapped mothers.
2. Accessorize wisely and individualize your outfit by wearing colourful heels, a stylish belt, a silk scarf or a few strings of chunky beads. A few added touches will really make the outfit your own.

Down at heel

I'd love to be able to impart some invaluable DIY advice for those hideous moments when your heel snaps off, but unless you're in the vicinity of a cobbler or happen to have some extra-strength superglue about your person, there's only one real solution: carry a spare pair. Not a spare pair of heels – your bag would have to be enormous – but a relatively stylish pair of flats or low heels. Ballet pumps are really light, as are flip-flops and other summer sandals, but make sure they're in a presentable condition. It may seem silly to have an extra pair of shoes in your bag at all times, but you'll be so grateful at the end of a long day or night.

Of course, if all else fails and the heel is broken cleanly, you could always snap the other heel off for an instant pair of uncomfortable flats ...

3. Which shapes work for you?

An outfit might look totally stunning on a friend of yours but slightly odd when you try it on yourself, and this is all down to variance in body types and shapes (see p.20). Although it's good to break the so-called fashion rules here and there, body shapes do present us with certain boundaries if we are to make the most of our best features (and minimize the effect of any features we're less fond of). We all have assets we're not keen on, but equally we all have strong areas, too. Women with short legs can often have a trim waist, for instance, so the solution here would be to elongate the legs by wearing wedges or heels and to make the most of the waist by wearing a stylish belt or fitted top. Easy!

Here are some basic guidelines:

HOURGLASS

AVOID:

- ★ Billowing tops that hide your enviable waist
- ★ Volume around the hips and thighs

GO FOR:

- ★ Fitted tops that accentuate your waist and cleavage without being too tight
- ★ Belted knee-length coats
- ★ Big belts that make a feature of your waist
- ★ Heels, which will accentuate shapely legs and hips

PEAR

AVOID:

★ Tent-like disguise pieces, which will only accentuate your thighs or bottom

GO FOR:

★ Styles that either raise or lower your waist, to make less of a feature of your thighs. Tops that fall on your hips worn with a (loose) low-slung belt will lower your waist, while cropped cardigans or jackets will raise it.
★ Flamboyant detail on your upper half
★ Items that work with your figure rather than disguise it. High-waisted pencil skirts may sound terrifying, but they can actually be very flattering if you pull the look off confidently.
★ Knee-length tailored dresses or A-line skirts, as well as simple knee-length coats

APPLE

AVOID:

★ Fussy details such as bows, frills and ruffles, especially around the neck or waist
★ Smock-style tops or dresses, which can create a ball-like impression on top
★ Cap sleeves or tight sleeves, if you have large upper arms
★ Gathered waists on trousers and skirts, as they only add volume

GO FOR:

- ★ Wide-legged trousers that fall to reveal just the tip of your shoes, and help to slim and elongate your legs
- ★ Heels, especially when worn with the wide-legged trousers described above
- ★ Clean, simple cuts for trousers and skirts
- ★ V-necks and chunky necklaces help divert attention from any areas you're less keen to emphasize

RULER

AVOID:

- ★ Tight skirts or trousers if you don't want to draw attention to a flat bottom
- ★ Trousers that neither taper nor flare, as they'll augment the 'ruler' appearance

GO FOR:

- ★ Tops with volume tucked into tight-fitting trousers or a skirt (if you *are* comfortable wearing them), which will create the illusion of a shapely figure
- ★ Thick fabrics such as velvet, cord and tweed – not many people can get away with this
- ★ Pleated or flared trousers and gathered waists
- ★ Billowing shapes, such as smocks and fussy skirts (puffball, ballerina, ruffles)

PETITE

AVOID:

- ★ Horizontal stripes, which create the impression of a shorter body
- ★ Baggy trousers, which also create a shorter appearance

GO FOR:

- ★ Dresses, which add length by not dividing the body into short sections
- ★ Empire lines
- ★ Heels worn with slim-fit trousers or skirts
- ★ Colour and accessories on the top half, which is the area taller people's eyes will instantly be drawn to

CLEAVAGE DO'S AND DON'TS

DO flaunt your cleavage where appropriate – that's what summer vests and evening dresses are made for.

DON'T hide a large bust behind enormous tops – this will have the opposite effect and draw attention to it. Wear something slim-fitting but not too tight for a more flattering look.

DO make sure your bra is the right size – it sounds obvious but when was the last time you actually got measured?

DON'T wear push-up bras to augment a small bust – they tend to create a squashed look. Opt instead for a padded balconette bra, which will offer a subtle boost and give a more natural shape.

DO wear detailed tops (pleats, frills and ruffles) to add volume to a flat chest.

4. Must-have wardrobe essentials

The first temptation when one of those 'Oh God, what on earth will I wear?' moments rears its ugly head is to dash out and buy a new outfit. It's certainly an easy solution, albeit an unnecessarily expensive way to manage your wardrobe.

A more effective (and hassle-saving) plan is to maintain a stock of wardrobe essentials – versatile garments that can make repeat appearances with the help of some cunning accessorizing or mixing and matching. Next time you're in town with some cash to splash, it might be worth purchasing something for your core collection rather than something so unique you can only wear it once.

Here are some suggestions:

SMART

LBD (LITTLE BLACK DRESS): One of the most versatile garments you can own, and there will *always* be an occasion to wear it, accessorized differently each time

BLACK TROUSER SUIT: A classic cut that can be worn to a job interview, meeting or funeral

CRISP WHITE FITTED SHIRT: Will look great with jeans, but is equally smart under your black suit

PENCIL OR A-LINE SKIRT: Can be dressed up or down, with a smart or casual top, heels or pumps

CASUAL

WELL-FITTING JEANS: Absolutely invaluable for day-to-day use as well as casual evenings out

'DECENT' TROUSERS: For when you want something slightly less casual than jeans

PLENTY OF SLIM-FIT LONG- AND SHORT-SLEEVED T-SHIRTS IN BASIC COLOURS: No explanation needed, really – you'll wear them every day

STYLISH CARDIGAN: Choose a dark colour if you anticipate wearing it very often (over a T-shirt, for instance) or something bright for occasional wear over your white shirt

SMART-CASUAL JACKET: A style that doesn't date easily will transform you skirt or trouser options in a flash.

SHOES

BOOTS AND FLATS: For everyday use

STRAPPY SANDALS: A neutral colour such as black, gold or silver will mean they go with most eveningwear and can be worn with different combinations

'INTERVIEW' SHOES: Comfortable, presentable heels or flats you can throw on for important meetings

MISCELLANEOUS

ACCESSORIES: And lots of them – swanky pieces as well as the cheaper, colourful variety. See p.94 for more on accessories.

GOOD COAT: A coat can make or break an outfit. Since they can be rather pricey and generally need to see you through a few seasons, it's worth investing in one that looks great with almost everything. If knee-length skirts or dresses and trousers are your staple, a knee-length coat is probably the best choice. If you're a fan of long skirts, however, a knee-length coat will just make you look like a vicar in flowing robes, so it's probably best to opt for a jacket or cape-style coat. Consider a neutral colour that will go with everything if your budget won't stretch to more than one coat.

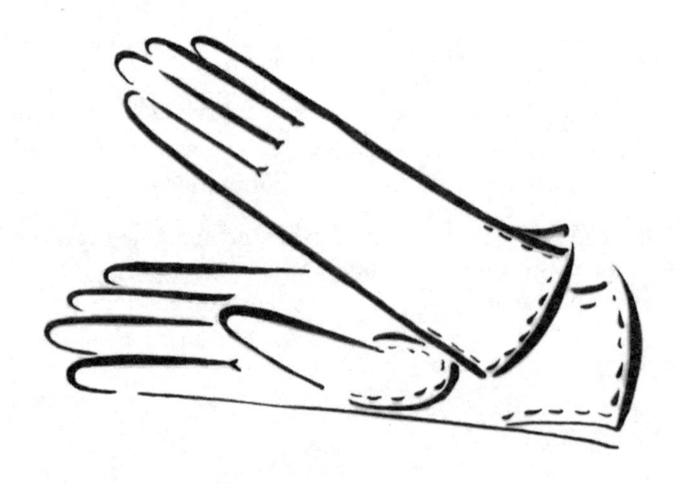

5. Are you returning to work?

Since you were last in work, fashions may have moved on a bit, but the two basic workplace rules remain unchanged:

★ What is the dress code?
★ What are you happy and comfortable wearing within those limits?

ON YOUR FEET ALL DAY?

You definitely need to wear flat shoes as often as possible. Heels add an instant touch of glamour to any outfit but your feet won't thank you if they spend every 9 to 5 squashed into gorgeous but impractical shoes. If you need to look smart, ballet pumps are a great choice as they're incredibly comfortable and pretty much always in fashion. Alternatively, go for knee-high boots with a flat or medium heel.

IS IT A SMART OFFICE?

Smart offices don't give you much room for manoeuvre as far as individuality is concerned, but just be grateful you don't have to wear the same old thing every day, as men do. There are plenty of ways in which you can make a trouser suit more unique: wear ballet pumps (yes, them again – they're invaluable) every now and then instead of heels, perhaps choosing a colourful pair that match your necklace and earrings.

IS IT A CASUAL OFFICE?

Lucky you! Offices are generally becoming less stuffy, especially for workers who don't come into contact with clients

HOW TO MAGIC AWAY NASTY STAINS

Chewing Gum

This tip will come in handy on a monthly basis for those with little ones, although ironically I only discovered it after having sat in chewing gum myself – while wearing a brand-new dress. Stick the offending garment into a carrier bag and put it in the freezer overnight. By morning, the chewing gum will come straight off.

Glue

Very similar to chewing gum – just much, much stickier. Whatever you do, don't put the garment through a wash in an attempt to soak the glue out – it will just become even more embedded in the fabric and you'll never get rid of it. Put the garment into the freezer overnight, and the majority of the glue should peel off in the morning. If there's any remaining glue, try placing a piece of brown paper over it and then ironing it – with any luck, the glue will stick to the paper and melt right off.

Toothpaste

It's baffling that something as simple as toothpaste can create such hard-to-remove stains, but you'll be no stranger to discovering those annoying white splodges on the school uniform just as you're rushing out of the house. Cold water does nothing to the stain and scratching it just spreads the horror, but very warm water on a cloth seems to do the trick. The affected area will look wet for a while, but it beats having to change your child's outfit when you're already running late.

Red, Red Wine

Whether you're a wine drinker or not, this is the ultimate party nightmare. Wherever it lands – clothes, carpet, white cat – it immediately looks catastrophic. While we all know that white wine or salt can be used to combat the problem, most of us panic and start pouring both white wine *and* salt all over the place, and then scrubbing the whole mess into an unsightly pink paste.

The first thing to do is act quickly but calmly, following one of these two tried-and-tested methods:

1. On garments, lie the affected area flat to avoid the wine running and use kitchen paper to absorb as much of the excess liquid as possible. Then pour over a generous amount of white wine (take the garment off first ...) and leave it to soak for about 20 minutes. Wash the wine out under a cold shower, blotting the liquid out rather than scrubbing it. Then use a regular stain remover to wash the garment as normal. If you don't have any white wine to hand, or if it's too good to waste on cleaning, use soda water instead.
2. On carpets, sofa covers and other non-delicate materials, cover the area with a thick layer of salt and leave for half an hour. Hoover up the salt and most of the red wine should be removed along with it. Wash the area with plenty of cold water, again being careful to blot rather than scrub. Then wash the material with a regular stain remover or furniture detergent and keep your fingers crossed!

Both methods also work wonders with cola and orange squash.

on a regular basis, so you can pretty much wear whatever you like. Don't take it as an excuse to turn up looking like a student, though – there are plenty of ways to be chic within a casual remit. It's also lovely to have a designated 'work wardrobe' that's distinct from your evening and weekend clothes, so set aside a couple of skirts and some presentable trousers for the office, along with plenty of accessories.

6. Paint the town red. Or black. Or green.

What you wear on a night out will entirely depend on where you're going and what the weather's up to, so there are no hard-and-fast rules to adhere to. Whatever the occasion, however, there are loads of things you can do to spice up your look and make sure you're the most fabulous person in attendance.

DOWN THE PUB

Even in these often insalubrious and traditionally unglamorous surroundings, there's no need to look as if you just wandered in off the street, no matter what the rest of the clientele is wearing. If you have a pair of 'sexy jeans', wear those with a fitted shirt and boots. (If you don't have 'sexy jeans', get some pronto.) Take some time over your hair and make-up but go for a natural look, as if your fresh, gorgeous appearance requires zero effort. In short: find a naturally sophisticated middle ground between the dishevelled creatures propping up the bar and the OTT miniskirt-and-fake-tan crowd, and you'll be the first to get served every time.

DINNER-DATE WITH THE OTHER HALF

These can be rare occurrences when there are young kids to consider, so it's worth making the most of every opportunity. Think of these occasions as romantic dates of the sort you enjoyed BFK, and opt for somewhere couples-orientated and atmospheric. Your trusty LBD is perfect for this sort of outing, matched with some new accessories if you want to look different without breaking the bank. Your partner may need a bit of cajoling to wear his decent shoes or smartest shirt, but if you both agree to make an effort, think 'in for a penny, in for a pound' and do your utmost to impress one another.

COCKTAILS WITH THE GIRLS

Frankly, there's no point in going out for cocktails if you're not going to pretend to be the fabulous ladies from *Sex and the City* – I'm sure the cocktails actually taste different if you're sitting there in jeans and trainers – so encourage everyone to pull out their swankiest dress and heels. No excuses.

WINTER WARMERS

Whether it's a chilly night of fireworks at the kids' school or a drizzly weekend football match with your boys, there's no getting away from the fact that you have to wrap up warmly – but how to avoid looking like yet another sad parent in an oversized anorak and wellies? Fitted knee-length coats are a much more feminine option, teamed with a colourful woollen hat-scarf-gloves set. Knee-high leather boots with a low heel are an instant improvement on wellies. If there's a chance of rain, make sure you have a large, tastefully colourful umbrella to keep you dry and happy.

TOP TIP

If you don't get many chances to dress up for a night out, make up some excuses to do so with your friends or partner. Go to a new local bar, watch the latest must-see play, host a 1920s-themed dinner or birthday party – whatever it is that will persuade your circle of friends to get into the spirit of things and glam up.

7. Spring-clean your style

Have you ever had one of those moments where you open your wardrobe and stare in gloomy dismay at its contents? Fear not: it happens to us all. What you're suffering from is an extreme case of 'What on *earth* will I wear?', which is often only remedied by a complete wardrobe overhaul.

Now, buying a new set of clothes can be pricey; completely revamping your style even more so. Fortunately, this is something best done in installments, so there's no need to bankrupt yourself in one gloriously frenzied shopping spree. If you've decided to make a fresh start with your appearance, decide on your new look, make a list of desirable items and then introduce things gradually – a bold new item every fortnight until the look is complete. That way people will notice the change in your appearance but won't think they've caught you on your way out to a fancy dress party.

8. Accessorize, accessorize, accessorize!

Accessories really are a godsend when it comes to individualizing an outfit, not to mention disguising the fact that you're wearing the same LBD to this week's dinner party as you wore to last month's christening.

Accessories can make an outfit, especially if your taste in clothes is quite simple. It's definitely worth spending a bit of extra money on certain accessories. Cheap-looking shoes, for instance, can wreck an otherwise fabulous outfit. The point of an accessory, after all, is to lift an outfit, to enhance it – not to drag it down into unremarkable monotony.

SHOES

We tend not to think of shoes as 'accessories' because they're such everyday items – we pretty much can't go anywhere without them – and as a result it's all too tempting to throw on any old pair that happen to be near the front door. But shoes really can make or break an outfit, by adding colour, elegance, detail and height.

It's good to have shoes in a variety of colours – or at least not all black – and in a variety of styles (flats, heels, boots, sandals). If you don't have the shoe budget of Imelda Marcos, however, try to find one really special pair of colourful, versatile heels – try red or emerald green for a change, two striking colours that go with many other shades. Avoid shoes that look cheap (whether or not they actually are) and avoid shoes that will quickly go out of fashion. It's far better to invest in a really decent pair that will last a few seasons. And remember it's much cheaper to re-heel shoes than to buy new ones.

BAGS

While some women have a bag to match every pair of shoes, others consider this a cardinal fashion sin. To be honest, it really is entirely up to you, but just be aware that accessories that look as if they've been bought as part of a set can come across as rather try-hard. That said, there's absolutely nothing wrong with opting for all-red accessories to go with your LBD – you'll just look more imaginatively stylish if it's obvious you've pulled the pieces together from various sources.

Bags have become more of a feature in recent years, growing in size and getting more vibrant in colour, so don't be afraid to choose one that's a little bit 'out there'. Bags that clash slightly with your outfit or other accessories are fine, too, so long as they're stylish and likely to garner compliments. Think of a new handbag as an investment buy, rather like a new pair of shoes, but don't splurge your entire budget on the one item: a huge daytime bag won't work with eveningwear, and a clutch purse is no good for the daily commute.

JEWELLERY

There are two main categories here:

- ★ timeless investment pieces
- ★ the costume/fake variety

Both have their place. Every woman deserves to have a collection of fine jewellery – well, you need to be able to pass things down, right? – but you don't need a huge hoard of it. There are a few basics that you'll be able to wear time and again, such as pearl or diamond earrings or an elegant gold chain.

These items obviously come with a downside – the price tag – so if you see something you really like but can't afford it, tactfully encourage your partner and friends to club together for your next big birthday. Alternatively there are some excellent fakes on the market these days; they too can be a little on the pricey side, but it's worth spending that little bit more to find fakes that don't look like fakes.

Think about your best physical attributes, and choose jewellery that will draw attention to them. So, for example, if you have a fabulous cleavage, you might want to wear a drop-pendant necklace or a beautiful brooch. Do you have gorgeous hands? Try an outlandish dress ring. If your style is more sporty, how about a silver wrist-cuff?

TOP TIP

The rules about not mixing gold with silver or pearls with other stones have long passed and it's now safe to mix and match – sometimes the more varied the better.

WATCHES

The only thing to bear in mind here is that metallic straps outlive leather ones and don't look as shabby as they age. Personally, I'm a bit paranoid about timekeeping and hate to be late, so I often wear a man's watch because it's so much easier to read. Its chunkiness is also slimming on the wrists.

BELTS

When you're standing in front of the mirror wondering whether your outfit needs a certain *je ne sais quoi*, a belt will often do the trick. A plain and simple pencil dress punctuated by a cute, slim belt can look so stylish cinched in at the waist. Belts can also add that dash of colour your outfit might need. Alternatively, for a more laid-back style, try a wide, low-slung belt worn at hip level over a shirt and jeans. Whatever you do, though, never ever fasten a belt too tightly. The same belt worn more loosely will look fifteen times more fabulous.

HATS

Hats aren't for everyone; a lot of women are convinced hats don't suit them, while others lack the confidence to carry them off. Annoyingly, though, the mere sight of a woman in a stylish-looking hat is enough to send most of us into a bout of hat envy, so it really is worth giving them a whirl, even if you've been averse in the past.

Whether you're planning your outfit for a wedding or simply looking for something to keep the rain off, it's a good idea to take a trusted friend shopping with you. Hats are so rarely worn these days that they do make more of a statement than your choice of shoes or jacket, and you need to find the right one. Milliners will be able to offer proper hat-style advice, but the staff in larger department stores can be just as knowledgeable.

GLOVES

Gloves are often not categorized as accessories because they're so functional, and often so bulky. What's glamorous about a thick pair of fleecy gloves? The answer, of course, is 'nothing'. But away from the ski slopes, a pair of long satin gloves can add a touch of classic style to eveningwear – think Audrey Hepburn in *Breakfast at Tiffany's* – and will certainly lend

TWO WAYS WITH A PASHMINA

Pashminas are a great way of keeping warm and looking stylish at the same time. What's more, you can pick up perfectly decent-looking ones for next to nothing.

1. The Parisian knot

For this sporty-yet-chic look, take your pashmina and fold it in half lengthways. Then loop it around your neck and pull the two loose ends through the 'noose' to tighten. You can either have the ends falling in front or tuck them into your coat.

2. The shawl wrap

Simply drape the pashmina around your shoulders and upper arms, so that it falls around your elbows. Then tie a single knot and let the ends drape elegantly in front of you. This looks good over eveningwear, so long as the pashmina is of a good quality and compliments your outfit.

your outfit an air of mystique. If cocktail parties aren't your thing, invest in a decent pair of elegant leather gloves for those cold autumn afternoons on the school sports field.

SCARVES

Scarves are one of the most versatile accessories you can own. From the chunkier woollen variety that comes out in winter to the delicate neckerchief *à la Parisienne*, they can serve a multitude of purposes. If you don't have a necklace that suits your outfit, try a small neckerchief; if you're worried about show-

10 SAVVY SHOPPING TIPS

1. **Don't go shopping when you're in a bad mood.** If you're irritable to start with, clothes, shop assistants and crowds will just tip you over the edge.
2. **Don't go shopping when you're feeling unattractive.** If you've put on a few excess pounds over Christmas, for instance, don't hit the January sales straight away. Trying on clothes that ought to be your size but inexplicably don't fit is one of the most rage-inducing aspects of shopping. Don't taunt yourself by buying clothes that are a size too small, in anticipation of losing the weight. The whole experience will be so much more enjoyable if the item actually fits you in the changing room.
3. **Use the internet.** When internet shopping first came about, I wasn't at all interested. As far as I was concerned, you couldn't beat the thrill of bagging a bargain right off the rail. But with young children to look after, internet shopping has proven rather a lifeline in terms of getting my weekly shopping fix. Not only can you shop around the clock and seek out the best prices, but you can also take your time making decisions, receive instant alerts about sales and bargains, and – the best bit – fantasy-shop: fill your basket to your heart's desire and don't spend a single penny unless you're certain you want to. Most online retailers have very easy-going returns policies these days, so you can send unflattering items back for free.
4. **Don't buy something just because it's on sale.** Would you have wanted it at full price? A cheaper price tag won't make it look any different once you're wearing it, so don't get carried away.

5. **Don't spend beyond your means.** If you have limited funds, make sure that you buy your basics first, and then allow yourself a couple of key investment buys when the sales come around. Plunging yourself into unmanageable debt will soon take all the fun out of shopping, so stay focused!
6. **Trust your instincts.** If you fall in love with something and can afford to buy it, go for it. It's incredibly frustrating to return a week later and find the line's been discontinued. If you can't live without it, don't.
7. **Buy in bulk.** If you find a garment that works for you, it can often be worth buying two – perhaps in different colours. You could keep the second one aside to wear once the first one 'dies'.
8. **Don't obey the sales assistants.** They mean well, but their job is to increase sales, not to debate whether the outfit you're trying on will clash with those party shoes you have sitting at home.
9. **Avoid shopping in bad weather.** Traipsing around the shops with your shoes full of rainwater, your glasses smudged, your umbrella out of control, your hair a wild, windblown mess and the ends of your trousers sopping wet will do nothing for your confidence or positivity when you confront your appearance in the changing-room mirror. At the first sign of grey skies, seek refuge in the nearest café with a good book and a calming cuppa.
10. **Don't get too much of a good thing.** Shopping for a couple of hours can be invigorating and a lot of fun, but there comes a point when enough is enough. Aim to go home on a high rather than bored and irritable – after all, you don't want to end up resenting the shops, do you?

ing off your neck or décolletage, how about making a feature of an elegant silky scarf? Ditto if you need to draw attention away from a top that's seen better days.

TIGHTS

Black tights can really help elongate short legs and create an overall slimmer look. But if you're wearing all black already and are feeling brave, try out red, navy, purple or dark green tights, which will really add a splash of individuality to your outfit. There are so many designs and styles available now – there's no longer any excuse to pull on the faithful old forty-denier black opaques.

9. Don't dress your age

Once upon a time, there were very strict rules where clothing for 'older' women was concerned, but thankfully they have become ever more diluted with the passage of time. Nowadays, there are no rules as such – more a silent code of conduct. Granted, there are certain 'youthful' items of clothing that look less glamorous on older bodies – boob tubes spring to mind – but why should clothes be labelled with an acceptable age-range? Surely if something suits you, you have every right to wear it?

There really are only three things you need to bear in mind if you're unsure:

★ Does the outfit suit you?

★ Do you feel comfortable wearing it?

★ Can your teenage daughter bear to see you wearing it without dying of embarrassment?

If the answers are yes, yes and yes – go ahead!

The truth of the matter is that we don't have to be frowned upon for wearing plunging necklines into our fifties or miniskirts into our sixties or jeans into our seventies if we have the body and confidence for them. Hollywood has helped pave the way, with ageing stars looking every bit as gorgeous on the red carpet as their twenty- and thirty-something counterparts. Most women have a profound understanding of what they can and can't get away with by the time they enter middle age, so ignore stuffy advice to the contrary and wear the outfits that bring out the best in you.

10. Don't shop till you drop

I am what is commonly known as a shopaholic. It's really not my fault, though – it's hereditary. I didn't ask to be this way, but oh, the joy of shopping! It's like no other drug. I literally can't understand it when other women tell me they don't enjoy shopping – how on earth is that possible?

These shopping-haters do have a point, though. If you head out to the shops without a clear idea of what you're looking for and how much you can afford to spend, the seemingly carefree task can turn into a nightmare of temptation and gratuitous spending. So before you hit the shops, prepare yourself by making two lists:

★ What do I *need* to buy? Is anything in your wardrobe in need of replacement? Do you have an important event coming up? Even if you only write down which colour you'd like to wear more of, or which new shape of clothing you'd like to try, it'll save you a lot of time.

★ What do I *want* to buy with any leftover cash? 'The latest designer handbag' and 'a third pair of lovely heels' fall into this category.

...And Relax

Being a mum is a full-time job, whether or not you also have a career during the week. This makes it especially important that you take some time out whenever you can, or set aside some time to do things that allow you to take your Mum hat off. And this time out can be as relaxed or raucous as you like, depending on what you enjoy. Make the most of those occasions when the kids are at a sleepover or visiting their grandparents or on a school trip, and don't underestimate the Quality Time you can share with your partner on these rare occurrences ... Before long you'll be exuding an enviable serenity that'll have other mums wondering how on earth you do it.

10 WAYS TO TAKE TIME OUT

1. Sort out your social calendar

If your social life has dried up a bit since having kids, try to get it back on track by instigating nights out – or in – with the people you used to hang out with. It's vital to keep your friendships in good shape and it's worth making the effort to get your circle of friends together as often as you can. There will invariably be a gaggle of children to consider, but perhaps they could be looked after by the dads while the mums go out to play. If a long-lost friend has children of a similar age to yours, introduce the kids to each other; if they become friends, it'll make your own friendship so much easier to maintain.

TOP TIP

Establishing a regular social event is by far the best way to prevent your newfound friendships from drifting apart again. A monthly book club, film night or pub quiz might well do the trick, or, if you're feeling ambitious, get a group of friends involved in a *Come Dine With Me*-style round of competitive dinner parties!

2. Go on a date

When did you and your partner last go out on a date? The sort of date where you can dress up, go somewhere grown-up (whether it's the pub or the theatre), talk about anything and everything and come home late? It can seem impossible to find the time for dating when you have to feed and bathe the kids, read them a story, put them to bed and then repeatedly traipse up and down the stairs putting them to bed again!

This is precisely why a date every now and then can provide a much-deserved rest. For anyone thinking, 'What's the point of going on a date with someone I see every evening?' consider what proportion of your average Tuesday night can actually be labelled 'Quality Time'. By the time you both sit down, safe in the knowledge that the children are asleep once and for all, the evening has almost disappeared and it's practically time to turn in.

To get the most out of your relationship, it's important to be able to talk about things other than recorder lessons and

football practice, so plan ahead to arrange a candlelit evening, a dinner date or a weekend away. Don't wait for your anniversary – one solitary romantic dinner a year isn't at all glamorous, you know!

TOP TIP

Don't ban yourselves from talking about the kids when you're out on a date – they're such an integral part of your lives that it's impossible not to. Just make sure you cover some other ground, too.

3. Plan ahead

In the same way as working mums might keep a diary for scheduling appointments, meetings and lunches around home commitments, stay-at-home mums can also benefit from keeping a clear and fully updated diary in which details of all parenting and social commitments are stored. Obviously it won't always be full of swanky engagements, but write down any major jobs you need to complete, alongside parents' evenings, dinner parties and shopping trips, so that you not only come across as highly efficient should anyone ask you whether you're free next Thursday, but can also keep a handle on your working and social life, resulting in an all-round more relaxed and organized persona. Then, if you're having a bit of a dull or stressful day, your mood will be lifted by seeing that you have a special family evening, night out with the girls, coffee catch-up or a romantic date to look forward to.

THE FREEZER IS YOUR FRIEND

Doesn't sound very glamorous, does it? But prepare to be amazed. When it comes to handy little kitchen hints that save you a whole lot of time and money, the freezer is a veritable goldmine.

★ Rather than waste the remains of a bag of fresh herbs – they're expensive enough – freeze them instead. Better still, if you have the time, chop the herbs finely and then freeze them, ready to throw into your next soup or stew. Make sure you label the bag before putting it in the freezer!

★ Is that pricey bottle of wine a bit corked? Pour it into ice-cube trays or empty yoghurt pots and freeze it for use in cooking. It may not taste great now but should work absolutely fine in your next chili con carne or risotto. Once you've done that, nip out round the corner for a replacement bottle and get back to enjoying your evening.

★ If you have some leftover strawberries or raspberries you're not going to finish any time soon, run them under the tap and chop off any dirt/stalks, and then freeze them in a Tupperware container. They will serve as impressively swanky ice cubes the next time you have the girls round for cocktails (see p.120), make a fruity smoothie (see p.127) or host a summer BBQ.

★ Significantly reduce the amount of bread you waste by putting loaves into the freezer before they go stale. Frozen bread is perfectly good for toasting, as long as it's sliced before it goes into the freezer. The same applies for bagels: slice them before freezing and then whip them out and toast them at a later date.

4. Keep fit

You don't need to belong to a fancy gym to be a fit and healthy individual: eating the right foods and doing the correct exercises will do you just as much good. The great thing about exercise is that it can be done on your living room floor and needn't be more expensive than the cost of a yoga mat and a DVD. Try a few different types of workout at home to see which exercises you enjoy and get the best results from. Once a fifteen-minute step or yoga session is incorporated into your daily routine, it's surprisingly difficult to give it up.

The ideal exercise regime should incorporate the following three aspects:

1. **Cardiovascular endurance:** Includes swimming, cycling, walking and step-aerobics

2. **Building strength:** Includes gentle weights and other gym-style machines

3. **Flexibility:** Includes stretching exercises such as yoga, Pilates or Callanetics

If you feel that, no matter what you eat or how much exercise you do, nothing will shift your extra pounds, it's possible you're eating the wrong foods or doing the wrong sort of exercise for your body type. Refer to p.21 to find out which type of body you have, and then try some of these shape-specific exercises.

ENDOMORPH

You tend to put on weight all over, possibly due to too much sugar and fat in your diet, snacking between meals, and not getting enough of the right sort of exercise. Weight-gain can occur gradually over a long period of time and, unless you start eating and exercising properly, it can take absolutely ages to lose weight.

Endurance exercise is perfect for you – walking, running, swimming and cycling, for instance. You should try to build up to a forty-minute workout two or three times per week, not forgetting to include some cardiovascular and stretching exercise, too. A decent step-aerobics DVD will help immensely, as will dancing and Pilates. Personally, I found that three months of Pilates totally transformed my body and made me realize the benefit of exercise for the first time.

Cut down on foods high in sugar and fat and eat more protein-rich foods, such as meat, fish and eggs. Avoid snacks between meals – make sure your meals contain enough carbohydrates (bread, pasta, rice, potatoes) to keep you going – and drink your two litres of water each day to keep you full and flush out toxins. If you need to snack, eat some fruit with low-fat yoghurt or raw vegetables dipped in low-fat hummus. Don't cut down drastically: for the best results, take your time and gradually correct bad habits.

A MORNING WORKOUT

Lunges

(Thighs and bum)

You will need a couple of weights: either two medium dumbbells or two regular tins of beans.

1. Start in a standing position, holding one weight in each hand, and with your hands at your side.
2. Take one large step forwards, bending your front knee so that your body weight is on your front foot.
3. Your back knee should be lowered slightly so that it is about 15cm from the ground.
4. Hold this pose for a few seconds and then return to a standing position by pushing yourself backwards using your front leg.
5. Repeat ten times, alternating between legs.

Standing Leg Curls

(Thighs and bum)

You will need a regular straight-backed chair.

1. Holding onto the back of the chair, raise one foot off the floor, bending your leg back.
2. Without using your hands or arching your back, keep bending your leg back behind you so that your foot moves towards your bum. Hold this position for a few seconds and then relax.
3. Repeat ten times, alternating between legs.

Bench Crunches

(Abs)

You'll need either a low bench or a sturdy coffee table.

1. Lie on your back, with your bum close to the bench or table and your lower legs resting on its surface, so that you form a sort of zig-zag shape.
2. Hold your arms out in front of you, towards your knees.
3. Take a deep breath and then contract your abdominal muscles as you curl your torso upwards, so that your back is raised about 10cm from the floor.
4. Hold this position for a couple of seconds and then exhale and relax.
5. Repeat ten times.

Side Bends

(Oblique muscles – waist sides)

You'll be needing your dumbbell or can of beans again.

1. Stand with your feet hip-width apart. Hold a weight in your left hand and put your right hand on the back of your head.
2. Bend slowly to the left.
3. When you feel a stretch in your oblique muscle (at the side of your waist), hold the position briefly and then use that muscle to push yourself back up to a standing position.
4. Repeat ten times and then swap sides.

MESOMORPH

Your metabolism is fast and you can therefore lose weight fairly easily. If you *do* put on weight, it's probably got something to do with your lifestyle. Make sure you keep active and eat a balanced diet.

As your problem area is the abdomen, yoga, Pilates or Callanetics are perfect for you, alongside some cardiovascular and strength-building exercises. Swimming and dancing are good for keeping a trim, toned waist, as are sit-ups.

Ready meals can be your enemy as they tend to be overprocessed and make you gain weight on the abdomen. Home-cooked vegetables, meat and fish are far better options, but avoid pulses, cakes and dairy products. Start the day with a hearty breakfast and reduce your meal sizes as the day progresses, so that you end the day with a light dinner. Breathing exercises can help ease any indigestion or bloating.

ECTOMORPH

You have a fast metabolism and lose weight easily – in many cases, far too easily considering your already-slim size. You don't tend to gain weight, but you don't tend to gain muscle, either.

Experiment with some (gentle) weightlifting and other strength-building exercises. You only need to do minimal cardiovascular exercise, but yoga, Pilates or Callanetics will help strengthen your muscles.

You can eat most things without it affecting your weight, but for the sake of keeping your skin, hair and nails in good condition, make sure you get a varied diet and eat plenty of fresh foods. A diet high in protein (meat, fish, eggs) will benefit your shape.

5. Be an early bird

Rather than falling asleep in front of some mundane TV drama every night, take yourself off to bed before you're totally exhausted. This'll give you the time (and energy) to make your pre-bed pampering treatments a routine – see p.60 for a nightly foot treatment and p.122 for more on night creams – as well as to read a few chapters of a good book or listen to some calming music in bed. As well as relaxing you and giving you some time to yourself, an early bedtime will ensure you fall asleep in the right place (i.e. your bed) and get a comfortable night's sleep. You may even find it helps you get up earlier in the morning to do some exercise or something else you enjoy, before the kids wake up and the day starts again.

6. Take a break

If you're a working mum, you'll already appreciate the benefit of a ten-minute break every now and then; they're just as important for stay-at-home mums battling against a pile of ironing and a bombsite of a playroom. It's easy to assume that, because you are at home, you are more relaxed or 'not really working', but a proper lunch break and some time off mid-morning and mid-afternoon will provide some much-needed mental and physical rest.

A proper break is one where you totally remove yourself from what you are doing, so drinking a cup of coffee while ironing does not constitute a coffee break! Leave whatever you're doing, sit down with a snack and a drink, and immerse yourself in something completely different. Your 'to-do' list will seem much more manageable after some time off.

7. Indulge in a bliss bath

Doing this every night will be something of a tall order depending on the age of your kids, but if you can fit in a luxurious bath once a week, you'll still reap the benefits. If you have the time, give yourself an at-home pedicure (p.61) or manicure (p.58) and exfoliate whilst relaxing in the bath. Put on some mellow music, light a few candles and have a fluffy towel and bathrobe at the ready. Basically, treat your bathroom as though it were your very own personal spa. With any luck, you'll start to see this as your regular slot of 'me' time and will benefit from it physically as well as mentally.

8. Have a massage

There's always a moment about two seconds into a massage when you wonder why on earth you don't do this more often. Well, cost is one very good reason. Full-body salon massages can be quite expensive, so they'll probably need to be reserved for a special treat. But if you think you'd benefit from a more regular spinal seeing-to, look into local massage courses where you and a friend or partner can learn how to massage one another. Seriously, there's nothing dodgy about these courses and you come away with loads of great tips on massage techniques and scented oils.

TOP TIP

On a smaller scale, get your other half to give your feet and ankles a gentle massage in front of the TV at the end of a hectic day – it's one of the loveliest ways to drift into relaxation.

9. Have a happy holiday

When you have young children, holidays tend just to be a matter of altered geography – you know, transporting all your Mum Tasks to a hotter climate. It's easy to forget that it's actually *your* holiday, too, and you can find yourself returning from some exotic location even more exhausted than when you went. So how can we make a holiday work for us as well as for the rest of the family?

Divide up a few of the holiday roles. This will depend on the ages of your children and the extent to which they are able to help, but if you can get them to sort out their own beach bags on a daily basis, it's a step in the right direction. Help them out on the first day, check what they've packed by themselves on the second, and then let them know that it'll be their job for the rest of the holiday. Older children can take some of the responsibility for ensuring younger ones have everything they need. Your husband can be put in charge of making lunchtime sandwiches and packing drinks, leaving you to ensure the kids are washed, dressed and covered in sunscreen before leaving for the beach.

Break up the day with a stroll. It's a good idea to break the day up with a wander, maybe into town or on a little excursion along the beach. If your kids are used to having an afternoon snooze at home, encourage them to do the same on holiday so that they don't end up grumpy at dinnertime.

Remember it's your holiday, too. So while the majority of the holiday might be spent on the beach or by the pool, an occasional cultural visit or shopping afternoon can make the trip fun for all the family.

Don't forget to relax! It sounds so obvious, but it can take a few days to wind down and get into the spirit of a holiday. Things you might worry about at home – the kids not eating healthily enough, for instance – often don't really matter on holiday, so relax the rules a bit and have fun.

CLASSY COCKTAILS FOR A GIRLS' NIGHT IN

The kids are with their grandparents, your other half's out doing whatever it is men do in their spare time, and you have the girls over for a soirée of stress-free fun. If ever there's a time to come over all *Sex and the City* and raid the liquor cabinet, this is it.

The following cocktails are really easy to throw together, depending on what you can get your hands on on the night. Don't bother buying all the fancy shakers and measures – just improvise.

Kir Royale

You will need:

2 teaspoons crème de cassis
Cava, prosecco or sparkling white wine (or Champagne if you're feeling flush)

Pour the crème de cassis into a Champagne flute and top up with your chosen bubbles. That's literally all there is to a Kir Royale and yet it's one of the most impressive cocktails you can serve.

Bellini

You will need:

2 parts peach juice or purée
4 parts cava, prosecco, sparkling wine or Champagne

Simply pour into a large wine glass and mix. Lovely with a raspberry sunk to the bottom.

Sea Breeze

You will need:

2 parts vodka
4 parts cranberry juice
2 parts grapefruit juice

Pour all three over ice into a tall tumbler. Ta-dah!

Cosmopolitan

You will need:

2 parts vodka
1 part Cointreau
1 part cranberry juice
A dash or two of lime juice

Shake all the ingredients together as best you can with plenty of ice, and then strain the liquid into glasses. For a final flourish, garnish each glass with a twist of lime rind.

(These recipes will make one drink apiece. Unless you're hosting a solitary cocktail party – which by the way is not advisable – multiply all the ingredients by the number of people in attendance and make a jugful.)

10. Sweet dreams

Scientists recommend that adults sleep for at least eight hours a night. 'Ha!' I hear you cry, 'The chance would be a fine thing.' And yes, mums with very young children will certainly struggle to achieve that. But when you do get the opportunity for a good night's sleep, make the most of it – your body and mind will thank you for it.

'Beauty sleep' is so named for a reason, and no cream in a jar can help you as much as regular, good-quality sleep. Contrary to appearances, your body is hard at work the whole time you're asleep, repairing damage that has occurred during the day, and renewing, rejuvenating, replenishing and rebuilding your skin, hair, muscles and bones. Sleep time is body-maintenance time, and your skin – your body's first line of defence – benefits the most. This is why many cosmetics companies recommend using a night cream – it's not all just sales mumbo-jumbo. A night cream can assist in the repair and re-plumping of skin, giving you a more youthful appearance come the morning. If you don't want to buy a specialist night cream, use your regular moisturizer instead.

Good sleep encourages good moods, since your store of energy will help you feel positive and upbeat. Likewise, your brainpower is given a huge boost by a decent night's sleep, with memory, motivation and general mental ability noticeably improved.

If you struggle to get a good night's sleep, experiment with these tips and see if they help:

★ Never go to bed straight from work, a stressful phone conversation or an argument. You will only lie awake seething with rage or anxiety. If you've been working late or otherwise increasing your stress levels, spend twenty minutes or so relaxing before hitting the pillow – watch a bit of mindless TV, read a magazine or a chapter of your book, or do something creative that you enjoy.

★ That said, avoid watching TV in the bedroom before bed. You'll inevitably fall asleep in an uncomfortable position with the disruptive sounds of adverts and late-night chat shows echoing around you, only to wake up confused and cramped at 5am.

★ Play some soft, soothing music in your bedroom as you drift off – as long as your partner doesn't object to your musical taste. Ideally you should play an album you don't know very well, so that you're not tempted to stay awake listening out for the rousing key-change at the end of your favourite song.

★ If you wake up in the night and can't get back to sleep, do something. Don't lie there worrying and fretting – everything always seems so much worse at 3am – but instead turn on a sidelight and read or do a crossword puzzle. You should find that you start to nod off soon ...

★ Always keep a glass of water beside your bed. There are few things more frustrating than waking up thirsty and spending ten minutes debating internally whether you can be bothered to creep down to the kitchen. A few sips of water will give you the energy to concentrate on sleeping instead.

Ooze Confidence

It's probably fair to say you were a different person BFK. You were younger, of course, and you were also more than likely in your most vivacious stage of life: fun-loving, brimming with confidence, wearing fashionable clothes and the latest make-up, going out whenever you fancied it and generally having a ball. Everything was about you, and quite rightfully so.

Nowadays, well ... it's not *quite* so easy to skip off for a night on the town. And if you were to get the opportunity, where would you go? With whom? Your favourite haunts may have changed hands, your best friends may be tied up in their own post-baby lives, and any notion of spontaneity seems well and truly scuppered. Many mums find themselves declining social invitations because it's all too much of a hassle. Some might even wonder whether, after a full day immersed in baby-talk or children's television, they've lost the knack – not to mention the stamina – for adult socializing, let alone *glamorous* adult socializing.

DON'T JUDGE A GLAMOROUS MUM BY HER COVER

Feeling fabulous when you're out and about is all a question of confidence. After all, glamour isn't all about outward appearance. Sure, high heels and make-up can certainly go a long way towards making you feel great, but true glamour is the ability to carry yourself in a self-assured manner, which comes with feeling good about yourself and feeling comfortable in your own skin – the way you probably did BFK.

So, in many ways, getting your post-baby social life back on track is rather like riding a bicycle: you've been out of the saddle for a while but you know you used to have the confidence to do it without a care in the world. The question is: how do you regain that va-va-voom?

A SPLENDID SATURDAY SMOOTHIE

Smoothies are really easy to make if you have a blender, and are a lovely, healthy treat for all the family on summery weekends. Just don't tell the kids they don't actually contain any sugar!

You will need:

500ml semi-skimmed milk (or soya milk – much healthier and nobody will be any the wiser)
500ml natural yoghurt
2 bananas
50g strawberries
50g raspberries
1 tablespoon honey

Whiz all of the ingredients together in a blender. Pour into large tumblers with some ice and a bendy straw – delicious.

R-E-S-P-E-C-T, FIND OUT WHAT IT MEANS TO ME

It's an unfortunate fact that being taken for granted tends to come with the mum's territory. Because we necessarily have to do certain things on a daily basis – prepare food, wash clothes, wipe surfaces – they become habitual and quickly develop into a routine. Everyone in the household gets used to the pattern, and, before you know it, 'it's Mum's job'. This attitude, in turn, becomes the norm for you, too, and you soon find yourself foregoing a movie night with friends because *somebody* has to do the ironing.

There are of course hundreds of Mum Tasks that can't be avoided – and plenty that you wouldn't *want* to avoid, given the chance – but, every once in a while, you need to shake things up. Let's face it: it's not so much the *doing* the jobs that's the problem, it's the lack of appreciation that grates. An occasional 'Thanks, Mum' or 'That was delicious, darling' wouldn't go amiss, would it? So why not delegate one of 'your' jobs to another member of the family for a week so that they can see how difficult, tedious or time-consuming it really is? They may not enjoy it but they'll certainly appreciate you all the more for it.

If your children are old enough to undertake the odd job here and there, you could even turn the cleaning/food preparation into a game (OK, it's tenuous, but stick with me), or offer some small remuneration for a job well done. This will have the double benefit of showing your family what a heroine you are and giving your children a sense of responsibility around the house.

If you foresee difficulties in convincing your family to pick up the hoover once in a while, the following tips might help.

★ **Draw up a rota for the next month,** with each person taking their fair share of each task. Include yourself in the rota to deflect any accusations of laziness. As long as you are fair, there should be no cause for complaint. See p.215 for some examples of jobs you might give to children of various ages.

★ **Make sure everyone knows exactly how to perform each task** and can take some pride in a job well done. If your child (or husband) is simply shoved into the kitchen with a sponge and a tea towel, it'll seem like a punishment rather than a reasonable request.

★ **If all else fails, throw money at the problem.** Offer pocket money or other rewards for jobs done promptly and without complaint. It may seem counter-productive to reward your family for taking on simple household tasks you could do yourself in half the time, but the very valid purpose of this exercise is to create a better balance in your daily life and instill a sense of responsibility in your kids.

SELF-ESTEEM: BECAUSE YOU'RE WORTH IT!

Being appreciated by those around you is all very well, but it won't get you very far in the glamorous-mum stakes if you are not, deep down, convinced of your own talents. Appreciating your own worth is absolutely vital as a mum, since – as we've already discovered – so many aspects of the job get taken for granted. When was the last time you thought, 'I did that really well'? If it's been a while – or if you're thinking, 'But I don't really do anything exceptional' – read on.

A SPRITZ OF GLAMOUR

Homemade face spritzers are easy to make, look and smell rather fabulous, and are really useful for keeping your skin fresh and hydrated during the day.

Choose an essential oil that you like. Rose, sandalwood or bergamot are all lovely. Mix a few drops with a little water and store in a small spray bottle (you can get these in most large chemists). When you feel you could do with a boost, just spritz to feel clean and refreshed. Perfect for the summer months, when skin gets rather thirsty.

It can be difficult to pinpoint your talents when day-to-day life has settled into a routine, a problem that most mothers face at some stage. Stay-at-home mums may feel that they lack the opportunity to get out and do anything noteworthy, while working mums might worry that they're too frantic to see anything through to completion. All of these niggling doubts take their toll on our confidence, often without us realizing it; we berate and criticize ourselves for not doing enough, when in truth we're already doing more than ought to be humanly possible – and then some.

Often it takes a specific event to hammer home the fact that your self-worth has taken a bit of a knock. Perhaps you've been invited on a hen weekend with a bunch of strangers, or realized an ambitious dinner party you've been promising is long overdue, or signed up for a course the start-date for which is looming. Things at which you wouldn't have batted an eyelid BFK can suddenly seem inexplicably daunting, leaving you too anxious to throw yourself into the event with gusto and glamour.

If you worked BFK, you most likely spent your days in meetings or dealing with clients and customers, your evenings socializing with colleagues, and your weekends shopping, lunching and partying with friends. I'd hazard a guess that life is a little different now ...

Fun as it sounds, the notion of having that lifestyle back again can seem quite daunting to mums returning to work or college after a few years at home with a baby, or once the kids have grown up and can take care of themselves. The good news is that you can deal with any nerves you may feel if you tackle them head-on. Think about the following ...

★ What *specifically* are you concerned about? Write down your worst fears about the event that is causing you to worry.

★ Re-reading your list of fears, are they based on a realistic appraisal of the situation or simply on the fact that you are out of practice?

★ Would your fears lessen or disappear if you could improve your confidence and self-esteem?

TOP 10 CONFIDENCE-BOOSTING TIPS

1. Walk tall

Address your posture and body language. This is a great place to start as it's actually very easy, you'll feel the benefit almost instantly, *and* you'll look fabulous.

CONFIDENCE AND SELF-ESTEEM

There are ultimately two main reasons why we might begin to dread things we formerly enjoyed:

★ Lack of confidence

★ Low self-esteem

Now, I know what you're thinking: surely self-esteem is the same thing as confidence? In fact, although there are many similarities, there are some important differences between the two attributes.

Confidence

Having confidence is really about having the courage to do things, no matter what the consequences. Confident people don't shy away from difficult situations and are likely to be the life and soul of a party. Celebrities often have high levels of confidence, but some – if gossip mags are to be believed – actually have very low self-esteem. Thoughts along the lines of 'What will people think?' and 'I'm too scared' indicate a lack of confidence.

Self-esteem

Self-esteem is your personal opinion of yourself. A healthy level of self-esteem equips you with a positive, realistic appraisal of your own qualities and abilities. This in turn contributes to a can-do attitude that enables you to deal with daily challenges without getting bogged down in pessimism. Low self-esteem can often make life seem very challenging indeed. 'I'm not good enough' and 'I won't be able to do it' are typical statements of low self-esteem.

Whatever your height and whatever your shape, your posture says a lot about you. Bad posture leads to all sorts of aches and strains, makes you appear smaller and less confident than you are, and can even prevent you from taking healthy deep breaths – so it's not surprising that adopting correct posture will work wonders for your alertness and general well-being.

Try standing up with your shoulders back, your back straight and your chin tilted slightly upwards. This may feel forced and rather Swiss-finishing-school-esque at first, but persevere: the more you practise, the more natural it will become – and the more relaxed you will feel. Keep this training up everywhere you go, from the school run to the supermarket or office. You'll be surprised what a positive effect it has on you; before long, others will notice, too.

If you also keep this in mind when you're sitting in front of your computer, you'll soon find yourself sitting in a much more upright position. This will lessen the strain on your back and shoulders as you type, and you won't get to the end of the day feeling like the Hunchback of Notre Dame.

TOP TIP

Imagine there's a string attached to the top of your head, and that some invisible puppeteer is gently pulling you upwards. It certainly works wonders for the supermodels…

2. Be heard

Try speaking a little louder than you normally would. There's no need to shout, but be aware of speaking to be heard. Even if you feel as if your speech sounds exaggerated at first, work on speaking with a clear voice, and concentrate on this until you get to the point where speaking with clarity comes easily and naturally to you. You might even throw in a few casual hand gestures to emphasize your speech.

Another useful tactic is what some life coaches refer to as the 'fake-it-'til-you-make-it' approach, which essentially entails *acting* like someone with greater confidence. The technique may sound a little absurd at first, but many people who have been advised to give it a go – for a nerve-wracking job interview, for instance – have reported a noticeable increase in

actual confidence as a result of having faked it. After all, if fake confidence produces good results, you can only be heartened and encouraged by the experience, and by your own ability.

If you think this technique might be useful in your own life, approach it as if you were taking on the role of a confident version of yourself in a stage production. Taking on this new persona, and keeping it up for a few weeks, will in time lead you to assume the role automatically and quite easily; in effect, you will have convinced yourself that you are a naturally confident person.

TOP TIP

The key thing here is simply to augment your own confidence, not to transform yourself into some sort of über-bitch who's totally unrecognizable to your husband, children, friends and colleagues. Introduce small changes one at a time, and you will gradually notice a positive difference.

3. Give yourself a pat on the back

Learn to appreciate your vast range of talents by focusing on the positive and not the negative. For the time being at least, forget the things you think you do badly and concentrate on the things you know you do well.

Writing a self-appreciation list is a great way to get started. List all the positive adjectives that best describe you, and ask your friends and family to help when you run out of ideas. You might be surprised by the things that end up on your list: thoughtful, fun, creative, an attentive listener ...

Next, write down all the things you are good at or that you manage to achieve in the course of a hectic day. Add to the list as often as you like and don't leave things out just because they seem commonplace or inconsequential; just as you praise your children for a job well done, pat yourself on the back if you've got through a huge pile of ironing, changed the bed linen in every room, got the kids to school in a neat and timely fashion every day for a week, or a whole host of other possibilities:

★ Telling the kids a bedtime story in a way that makes them laugh, perhaps by letting them fill in the blanks.

★ Making the kids' packed lunches before you head off to work.

★ Successfully answering one of your child's many 'But *WHY*?' questions.

★ Preparing a healthy meal for the family.

★ Swotting up on your maths or French verbs so that you can help with homework.

★ Having the time to sit on the sofa at the end of the day, guilt-free.

4. Confront your demons

Whether or not you were a social butterfly BFK, keeping your social life going becomes considerably trickier when you have young children in tow. With so many balls in the air, something's got to give – and, more often than not, that 'something' is your raucous nights out with the girls.

Lack of practice can leave you feeling as if you've forgotten how to be the life and soul of the party, but practice makes perfect. If you're nervous about a night out with a group of people you don't know very well, brush up on your current affairs when the kids are at school or in bed or read an up-to-date mag on your way there.

TOP TIP

Don't give in to anxiety and let lack of practice age you prematurely. When trying new things, remember that the vast majority of people *want* you to succeed – put your best foot forward and get on with it.

5. Don't worry, be happy

Don't underestimate the power of happiness: make time to be happy. This may sound ludicrous, but stop and think about it. Would you say you are a happy person? Or are you just too busy even to notice?

Well, you *should* think about it because your own happiness can have a profound effect on your family's happiness. A study by the University of Edinburgh found that 50 per cent of a person's happiness is partly an inherited characteristic and partly formed during childhood, while the other 50 per cent is down to the individual and his or her environment. In a nutshell: if you're feeling unhappy, you can do something about it.

Everyone deserves to feel happy and everyone needs to have some chill-out time. If you set some time aside for this, you'll soon see that it improves the quality of your home life.

TOP 5 HAPPY TIPS

1. Set aside as much time as you can to immerse yourself in something you really enjoy. Whether it's an outdoor hobby or getting your nails done in town, you should spend time indulging in something that helps you unwind.
2. Surround yourself with good company whenever you can. If you don't have the time or energy to host swanky parties, invite friends or family over for a casual evening – each person can bring an easy dish while you provide popcorn, wine and a DVD.
3. Be open and honest with people you are close to for more rewarding relationships.
4. Spend quality time with your family outside your home. Go to the park, spend a day on the beach, visit a castle … Whatever it is you all enjoy, just go out and have fun.
5. Control negative thoughts by turning them on their head and doing something positive to rectify them.

6. Empower yourself

It's very easy to feel duty-bound to sort out everybody else's happiness before your own, but before long you can find yourself running endless errands and performing endless favours, none of which you'd choose to do if you had the option. How can you possibly make the most of your free time when there's a lunch to attend, or your mother's dry cleaning to collect, or a work party at which you ought to show your face?

There is one simple, incredibly empowering answer to all these questions: just say no.

We've all been in the situation where we've grudgingly said, 'Yes, I'll be there' or, 'OK, I suppose I'm going in that direction anyway', when what we really want to say is, 'To be honest, I can't think of anything I want to do less.' While our intentions are admirable when we agree to do things just to make other people happy, the downside is rising resentment and stress, which simply won't do if we are to appear effortlessly glamorous.

Feeling empowered is all about setting boundaries and sticking to them. I'm not suggesting we always put ourselves first no matter what – nor that we actually go around saying, 'To be honest, I can't think of anything I want to do less' – but simply that we become diplomatically selective with the precious free time we have. It is perfectly acceptable to say 'no' if it's done tactfully:

★ 'I'm absolutely shattered – I'd really enjoy a quiet night in.'

★ 'I'm budgeting this month and just can't afford it.'

★ 'I'd love to help you but I simply don't have the time.'

★ 'I'm really busy this week but maybe some other time soon?'

These are all perfectly reasonable – and truthful – responses to less-than-desirable requests and invitations.

TOP TIP

It's probably best to introduce any changes in your general attitude gradually, lest your friends or colleagues become offended at your sudden lack of enthusiasm, but try it once and see how it feels.

7. Listen and learn

It's easy to forget that the art of conversation isn't all about talking: there's not much point in someone talking if nobody's actually listening. We all have days where we feel disinclined or uninspired to make sparkling, witty conversation, so why not simply listen to those who *are* in the mood for holding court? After all, everyone loves talking about themselves.

If you can prove yourself a good listener by asking questions and interjecting with the occasional 'How awful!' or 'What was he *thinking*?', the other person will come away from the conversation thinking they've had a great chat. And, what's more, they'll probably prove just as attentive next time you *do* feel like launching into an anecdote.

8. Have fun

When was the last time you did something for the simple reason that it interested you? Too many of us let our interests or hobbies slide because we think we don't have time or because we get used to being too busy. But we're never too busy to collect the kids from school, take them to clubs, and shop for presents for their friends' parties, are we? We *make* the time to do those things because they are important, but why is it different when it comes to our own needs?

Ask yourself what you enjoyed doing BFK. Are you a starved social butterfly or a craving culture vulture? You may not have quite as much time to spare these days, but it's vital to keep a strong sense of your own individual personality

LAST-MINUTE AFTERNOON TEA

A friend announces at a moment's notice that she'll swing by for an afternoon catch-up while the kids play. It certainly beats doing the hoovering, but what on earth will you serve for afternoon tea? There's no need to rush out to the bakery – you can knock up an afternoon tea in less than an hour, trust me.

For an easy Victoria sponge, you will need:

170g margarine
170g self-raising flour
170g caster sugar
3 large eggs
1 teaspoon baking powder
Jam
Whipped cream

- ★ Heat the oven to 190°C/Gas Mark 5 while you grease two eight-inch cake tins.
- ★ Throw all the ingredients together and mix them until they form a smooth paste.
- ★ Divide the mixture equally between the two tins and place them both in the oven for about 20 minutes, or until the sponge feels springy to the touch.
- ★ Cool the two sponges on a wire rack, after which you can slather one side of each with jam or whipped cream.
- ★ Stick the two jammy/creamy sides together, tidy up the edges a bit and then sift some icing sugar over the top.
- ★ Decorate the platter with some fresh fruit if you want to look a bit fancy.

While the sponge is cooling down, you can turn your attention to some sandwiches with a difference. It doesn't matter what you fill the sandwiches with, and at short notice you might only have cheese at your disposal, but you can make them look instantly more appealing by using a cookie cutter to create some fun, kid-friendly shapes. If you don't have any cookie cutters, just trim the crusts off and cut into three strips to make delicate finger sandwiches. Present on a large platter with a bowl of cherry tomatoes or carrot and cucumber batons, which will add a splash of colour.

Now all you need to do is get the kettle on!

despite your other obligations. Being glamorous isn't just about looking the part: you need to feel like a rounded, interesting person, too.

9. Be a copycat

Try emulating someone you admire. This doesn't mean be an outright copycat, but if there's someone whose poise or style you envy, study her (in a non-stalking manner) to work out what she does differently.

Does she speak in an engaging manner or carry herself elegantly? Does her body language radiate confidence? Is her tone understanding or her outfit carefully chosen? These are all things you can try yourself. Take some time to observe these traits and see if you can incorporate a unique take on any of them into your own personal style.

10. Use NLP

Neuro-Linguistic Programming might sound overly scientific for a book about glamour but it is in fact a really straightforward empowering technique. NLP is a practical approach to achieving results you desire in life through effective communication, and consists of three key elements:

N	**Neuro**	The mind and how we think
L	**Linguistic**	How we use language and how it affects us
P	**Programming**	How we sequence our actions to achieve our goals

NLP began as a study of exceptionally effective communication exhibited by successful individuals – the theory being that, if certain techniques have worked in the past, duplicating them will surely breed further success.

There are a number of ways in which NLP can be used in everyday life, but one of the main exercises people undertake is creating a positive rapport with others by observing and mirroring their language, gestures and poise. You might, for example:

★ Increase your own use of hand gestures when talking to someone who's physically expressive.

★ Mirror the tone and speed at which the other person speaks. (Mimicking their accent will prove less successful, however.)

★ Use vivid imagery when talking to someone who comes across as visual or artistic, as this will better enable them to imagine the scene you're describing.

Subconsciously, people are more at ease if they feel they are talking to someone who is similar to them, so this is a really simple way of breaking through someone's barriers and having more honest, friendly conversation.

Another vital facet of NLP is understanding yourself and thereby confronting the things that make you react in an unconfident manner. By visualizing the scenarios that alarm you – public speaking, for instance, or hosting a large party – you can work towards pinpointing the exact cause of your anxiety, and developing a calmer reaction. Essentially, try breaking each confidence-sapping scenario down into its individual parts, and then attack the ones that cause you to lose your nerve.

This is just a brief taster of a much wider subject, and there are many ways in which NLP can be adapted to your own personal situation. So if it sounds as if it might be of use to you, get down to the local library or onto the internet and start reading.

Be Inspirational

Now that we've addressed confidence and self-esteem, the next stop on our journey towards fabulousness addresses what to do with those valuable attributes. While a vital component of glamorous mumhood is impressing yourself with your own talents, an equally vital component is charming others with your engaging personality.

EXPRESS YOURSELF

Things might have changed since you had kids, and in all likelihood it's been a while since you were carefree enough to indulge in your own interests whenever you felt like it. There are, however, several small ways in which we can all keep our levels of cultural or specialist knowledge topped up. Be inventive and creative with whatever spare time you have, and make the most of every opportunity to learn something new or improve on the skills you already possess. All of these things make for great conversation topics when you want to leave a memorable impression.

TOP 10 INSPIRATIONAL TIPS

1. Have a specialist subject

If you had to appear on *Mastermind* tomorrow – it could happen – what would be your specialist subject? What are you good at and what really interests you?

If you are a 'jack of all trades and a master of none', why not change that? Choose something that you are good at or interested in and which, most importantly, you enjoy, and learn to master it. Whether it's writing, running, fire-breathing or building websites, it's great to know that you're passionate about something, and to have something that's really *yours*.

2. Recommend good books

There are few things that beat losing yourself in a really good novel. Carry a paperback in your handbag for those lost moments in the doctor's waiting room, or when waiting for a bus. There's nothing wrong with dipping in and out whenever you have five minutes.

But what to read? There are loads of places from which to draw your inspiration: bookshops, bestseller lists, newspaper reviews ... Better still, ask your friends or colleagues for recommendations – you never know who might prove to be a mine of excellent suggestions.

If you discover that others in your circle also love reading, why not start a book group? You can meet once a week or once a month – whatever suits your schedule – taking it in

THREE THRILLING BOOK CLUB CLASSICS

1. ***Rebecca* (1938) by Daphne du Maurier**: When a naïve young woman marries dashing older gent Maxim de Winter after a whirlwind romance, she has no idea what she's let herself in for. Back at de Winter's country estate, the new bride has to contend with an upper-class society determined not to welcome her, lingering reminders of her husband's deceased first wife Rebecca, and the cruel machinations of Rebecca's devoted housekeeper, Mrs Danvers. With an excellent twist or two, this novel is guaranteed to send shivers down your spine.
2. ***Chocolat* (1999) by Joanne Harris**: A mysterious woman named Vianne moves to a sleepy French village with her young daughter and opens the most exquisite confectionary shop, offering a mouthwatering range of tempting chocolates right in the middle of Lent. The local priest is outraged, especially once his congregation begins breaking Lenten vows to sample Vianne's 'sinful' chocolates. This is a beautiful story about passion and temptation, with a lead character who is arguably the ultimate glamorous mum – especially when portrayed by Juliette Binoche in the 2000 film version.
3. ***Notes on a Scandal* (2003) by Zoë Heller**: This is the story of Sheba, an enchanting but impulsive mother of two whose new teaching job brings her into contact with our narrator, embittered spinster Barbara. Although Barbara is delighted to have made a new friend, she becomes ever more jealous when Sheba begins an ill-advised affair with a fifteen-year-old pupil, with explosive results. This novel can't fail to spark an interesting discussion, but is probably best avoided if you happen to have a fifteen-year-old son …

turns to nominate a book and host the discussion, perhaps over lunch. This is a great way to kill three birds with one stone: expand or refine your literary tastes, enjoy some intellectual conversation, and have a great excuse see your friends over a coffee or, preferably, a glass of wine.

TOP TIP

Do an internet search for 'reading group questions' if you're not sure how to get the discussion rolling.

3. Do something totally different

As the children get older and spend more time in school, you'll be left with a lot more free time. For the most part, what you do with that time is entirely down to you. Great news, right? Right?

Well, not necessarily. While some mums who suddenly have loads of free time on their hands welcome the freedom to let their hair down and do what they want, others get totally phased, and at first might have feelings of being surplus to requirements ('They don't need me any more').

But this is no time for sinking into a period of mourning: it's your chance to get out there and fulfill some of the ambitions you've had on the back burner in recent years. This is an exciting time, and the world is – for large chunks of the day, at least – your oyster. Take the opportunity to learn or do something totally different each day, no matter how small. Here are some suggestions:

- ★ Go through your wardrobe and sort out the things you can revive or adapt.
- ★ Learn to drive, play the trombone, do flamenco – whatever it is you secretly wish you could do.
- ★ Channel the self-sufficiency spirit of the 1940s and get creative in the garden – growing your own fruit and veg is surprisingly rewarding.
- ★ Do volunteer work at a local charity shop or school.
- ★ Get competitive and join a club: tennis, photography, poker, knitting ...

There are so many ways in which you can put your newfound free time to excellent use, and get to the end of each day feeling fulfilled and fabulous.

FENG SHUI YOUR HOME

'Feng shui' is a term that's been bandied around by interior designers for a few decades now, but what on earth is it actually all about? Well, 'feng' is from the Chinese for 'wind', while 'shui' means 'water', and the discipline is all about balance and the positive flow of energy ('chi') around buildings and other spatial arrangements. If you get it right, your home – and, by association, you – will exude calmness and harmony.

Failing that, you can at least *tell* people your home is feng-shui-friendly, which ought to garner a few glamour points.

Hallway

The entrance to your home should be welcoming and have a positive feel to it. Just a few touches and a little effort will set the tone for the rest of your home.

1. A bamboo plant positioned at the entrance to the hallway is meant to be a sign of good luck and success. It also helps to break up some of the hallway's angles and straight lines, which create a negative energy.
2. If you keep shoes near the front door, make sure they are kept out of sight. As well as looking unwelcoming, they can infect the incoming chi with unwanted odours, thus causing negative energy to flow around the house.
3. Avoid clutter, which not only looks unwelcoming but is also said to create obstacles for the uninterrupted flow of chi.

Lounge

This is the heart of the house, where you sit to relax, socialize and spend quality time with your family, so it's important to get the flow right. There's no need to chuck everything out (although a red sofa will apparently bring you stress), but a little careful positioning of furniture is meant to help enhance the flow of chi.

1. Have things around you that inspire, stimulate or make you feel happy, such as art, fresh flowers and photographs. Remove any dead flowers as soon as possible.
2. Bright overhead lighting is disruptive. Instead opt for soft lighting around the room, maybe in the corners.
3. Try to place chairs and sofas with their backs to the walls. Don't fill your lounge with too much furniture, but use what you do have to break up the straight lines and angles in your décor.
4. Goldfish, the descendents of koi carp, bring prosperity when grouped in threes. Water, meanwhile, attracts chi and maintains its continuous circulation. Don't keep fish in the kitchen or bedrooms, however, as their presence here can cause material loss. When your child's pet goldfish dies, you'll be pleased to hear it has taken some of the negative energy meant for you away with it.
5. Open your windows for at least twenty minutes each day, to allow the free flow of fresh chi.

4. Learn from your kids

Kids seem to be branching out into so many different ways of learning from a really early age these days. Then they bring work home to complete on their own, which can prove problematic if we aren't able to nudge them in the right direction when they get stuck. There are few things worse, at the end of a long day, than having to admit to your nine-year-old that you are not in fact an expert on the Industrial Revolution or the rock formation of volcanoes.

One way of helping your child, at the same time as learning something new yourself *and* saving face, is preemptively to ask your child to explain the homework topic to you. If they're unsure of something and you aren't immediately able to help, you can then look it up together. This, along with going to relevant museums or watching relevant documentaries, is a really easy and surprisingly fun way of revisiting long-lost subjects, or learning something entirely new. Just think: you'll be so accomplished by the time your kids leave school!

5. Get creative

If you were pigeonholed as 'sporty' or 'brainy' or 'always in the Naughty Corner' at school, you may well never have had the chance to explore your creative side, but it's never too late to start. You don't need expensive equipment or a degree in fine art to be creative; it's all about using the skills you have in a clever and imaginative way.

There are loads of ways in which you can stamp your own personality on everyday things, and give your friends and relatives something to marvel at in the process. Here are some easy suggestions:

★ **Make personalized greetings cards.** Stash anything that catches your eye over the course of the year, from patterned paper to funny photos, and create birthday cards that reflect the recipient's interests or personality. The brilliant thing here is that you don't need to be Renoir to put together something that's both touching and unique, and which will go down an absolute storm.

★ **Be imaginative around the house.** You don't always need to buy new bits and bobs to brighten up the house – often you can spice things up by using an ordinary object in an imaginative way. Fill a clear vase with shells, marbles, sweets, floating candles, sparklers or fairy lights; grow kitchen herbs in chipped mugs or colourful tins; make retro garden-party bunting out of those lurid old clothes lurking at the back of your wardrobe ...

★ **Make a photo album.** Creating an album is a satisfying and rewarding way to unleash your creativity. For a really touching gift that's guaranteed to impress and inspire others, make an album of shared memories for your best friend or sibling. Since albums are treasured more and more as time passes, your wonderfully personal gift will be talked about for years.

★ **Revert to your teenage ways.** Remember those lovingly crafted collages of dubiously coiffed singers and Hollywood stars you used to make in your teens? Well, it's time to dig out the scissors, mags and glue once more. Your tastes have probably – hopefully – moved on since then, but a handmade collage of funky illustrations or stylish designs can really brighten up a wall. You might even fill a picture frame with lots of small images made up of the same colour, so that people really need to study it to work out how you did it.

6. See the world

When the kids are young, holidays tend to be safe and designed with child-friendly activities in mind, so it's almost inevitable that most holidays blur into one another: sunshine, sand, swimming pool, ice cream, jellyfish sting – the usual story. This is not to say that holidays with young kids are dull – far from it – but it's lovely to be able to shake things up a bit once they're a little older.

Introducing your children to new places, new cultures and new experiences doesn't have to blow the budget, and you'll have plenty to talk about once you get home, too.

★ If you're tired of beach holidays, go camping. It needn't be a rain-sodden campsite in the middle of nowhere, either; there are plenty of sunny spots to camp across Europe and the United States. You could still be near a beach and pool, but have the added enjoyment of cooking over a portable stove and telling stories under a starry sky. If the kids are a little older, how about a horse-riding or surfing lesson on one of the days? Youth-hostelling is another cheap but very cheerful way to travel around.

★ If you can't afford to go away, have what has become known as a 'staycation' – a holiday at home. It might not sound very exciting, but you can challenge yourselves to do something new each day, whether it's visiting a castle, driving to the nearest bit of beach, eating an exotic takeaway or cycling along a river, with plenty of picnics en route.

★ Visiting a foreign city with a young child sounds daunting, but why should it be? In many ways, cities offer far more stimulating activities than your average beach, and if one attraction proves unpopular, move onto something else. You might be surprised at what your children enjoy.

If there's a trip you've been putting off until the children are older, give it some real thought before abandoning the idea. Is it really so impossible or could a nearby theme park and a couple of McDonald's trips make it fun for all the family?

7. Stay bang up to date

You don't need to pass yourself off as a political expert, but having a reasonable understanding of current affairs is both useful and interesting. Not only will you be able to relax and enjoy news-related conversations when they crop up, but you will also avoid those mortifying scenarios where you inadvertently prove you have no idea what everyone else is on about.

Don't be the quiet one in the corner – it simply isn't glamorous. If you find you are too busy to watch the news every day, get in the habit of turning the radio on whenever you're at home or in the car. And staying up to date isn't just about wars and political debates: sports news, film and book reviews, popular music, fashion and the classier end of the celebrity-gossip spectrum are all key components of the world around us, and you can pick and choose your topic of conversation depending on the other person's taste.

TIPS FOR TRAVELLING WITH YOUNG KIDS

Long journeys can be boring for all of us, but young children find them particularly tedious – which doesn't do much for our own stress levels. The best way to survive these journeys is to be prepared. Have a mental checklist of things to take or do to make the experience more enjoyable – or at least to make a dramatic reduction in the number of 'Are we *there* yet?'s.

1. You can never have enough wipes to hand. Sticky fingers, dirty faces, spilt drinks – not to mention travel sickness – are all par for the course.
2. Plan plenty of pit stops. Stop for toilet breaks before the situation becomes desperate, and stock up on water and little snacks if you're running low. If you're able to stop somewhere vaguely pleasant, a quick walk will stretch everyone's legs and delay the next tantrum by a good twenty minutes or so.
3. Take a few new toys and activity books with you and reveal them one at a time, to avoid boredom.
4. If possible, plan your route so that you pass an impressive castle, skyscraper or other landmark. Build the landmark up a bit, with as much exciting historical detail as you can gather, so that the kids are suitably amazed by the time you drive past.
5. Always keep a few plastic bags, changes of clothes, medicine sachets and a towel to hand (i.e. not at the bottom of the boot), so as to be prepared for any eventuality. A blanket cunningly placed on or near your child might encourage a welcome snooze, too.

If you have young children, make it your mission to know what music is in the charts, even if you have to look it up online rather than listen to the weekly countdown. There's nothing quite as shaming as having a group of eight-year-olds explaining emo rock to you, rolling their eyes as you ask how the Spice Girls are doing these days.

8. Be proactive

We're all capable of making grand plans and then letting them slide, whether it's New Year's resolutions or the latest fad diet, but when something is really worth doing, it's worth doing right. Whatever it is you choose to do in order to unleash your scintillating personality, do it wholeheartedly and without compromise.

The key to being proactive, really, is setting yourself achievable goals rather than announcing out of the blue that you're going to master Chinese or run a marathon. (If mastering Chinese or running a marathon *are* achievable goals for you, you've already got this point covered!) If, for example, your ultimate ambition is to run a marathon but you're no Paula Radcliffe, set yourself a series of realistic targets in order to work your way up:

★ Buy some decent trainers
★ Devise an easy local route
★ Go jogging twice a week
★ Go jogging four times a week
★ Compete in a 5k run, a 10k run and a half-marathon
★ Enter a full marathon

It looks so easy on paper! This is rather an extreme example but it does illustrate the way in which even a mad-sounding ambition can become reality if you approach it rationally and proactively. What's preventing you from fulfilling all the plans you had BFK? What's stopping you from doing all the things you loved before (well, you might want to give Saturday-night clubbing a miss), just less frequently or with more forward planning?

As mums we don't have many opportunities to be spontaneous, but when the chance does come along – grab hold of it. Be the sort of person who takes on a challenge, who says, 'Oh, let's do that – it'll be fun!' or who invites a friend round at the last minute if other evening plans fall through.

9. Don't try to have it all

Despite women's mags' insistence that modern mums can 'have it all', most of us simply don't have the time to feed and bathe the kids, clean the house, run a multinational organization, paint the town red every night *and* scale mountains at the weekend. The real key to 'having it all' is accepting that, in fact, we just *can't* have it all. Ultimately, we don't *need* to have it all in order to feel fulfilled.

A happy and glamorous life is one lived to the full, in which we make the most of every opportunity as it presents itself and have the courage to create new opportunities, too. We ought to strive towards being happy with our lives – with the odd adjustment here and there when necessary – rather than striving for the impossible and ending up disappointed and frustrated. Whether you're a working mum or a stay-at-home mum, getting the right balance between Mum Tasks and 'Me Time' is where it's at.

Experiment with the plan in the final chapter of this book to see how balanced you can get. If you can organize the various components of your life into a well-balanced schedule, you'll be one of the calmest and most enviably serene mums in town.

10. Have a positive attitude

A positive nature is one of the most desirable characteristics anyone can have. What's more, positivity is contagious. Have you ever been smiled at by a total stranger in the street and wandered away smiling to yourself, inadvertently passing the smile on to everyone else you see? In contrast, you've no doubt been served by a surly supermarket attendant or sworn at by an aggressive driver, and felt full of rage as a result. These examples show the incredible influence one person's attitude can have on everyone else around them.

POSITIVELY PERFECT

Research has found that positive thinkers are generally happier, healthier and more successful than their pessimistic counterparts. **Happier** because they have a more outwardly focused attitude, which gives them a greater capacity for appreciating life's small pleasures; **healthier** because they experience less stress and anxiety, thereby reducing their risk of heart disease and premature ageing; and **more successful** because they aim higher with their ambitions and are more persistent in trying to achieve them.

Whether you're faced with a stroppy child who refuses to eat their greens, a highly-strung friend who's looking for an argument or a pessimistic colleague who sees the cloud in every silver lining, exert your infectious positivity on the situation and lift the general mood. Try to avoid joining in with vicious gossip or pointless moaning – they'll do nothing for your own frame of mind – and instead work on remedying any areas of your life that might lead you into the doldrums.

TOP TIP

Misery breeds misery and happiness breeds happiness. Which feels better? Take it upon yourself to spread some cheer.

Appreciate the Small Things

'The best things in life are free' is a bit of an old cliché and the kind of thing your grandmother would say, but it really is true. In a world in which even something as simple as a family day out comes with a hefty price tag – travel expenses, entrance charges, lunches, sweets and souvenirs, dinner costs – it's easy to forget that fun doesn't have to be prohibitively expensive. But appreciating the small things can make a huge and noticeable difference to your general outlook on life, so, if you're feeling a bit low or unglamorous, look around you for some uplifting inspiration that needn't cost a penny.

10 WAYS TO LOVE THE LITTLE THINGS

1. Make a song and dance

I've said it before and I'll say it again: there's nothing quite as uplifting as having an impromptu jig around the kitchen while you're preparing dinner or doing the washing up. It also counts as a great bit of exercise, so there's really no excuse not to have the radio on non-stop. While you're at it, belt out a tune or two (assuming the kids aren't in bed or trying to do their homework in the next room). It's a strangely liberating experience, especially if you're normally a quiet person or work in a quiet office. You never know, it might even put you in the mood for a spot of karaoke next time you have a night out with your friends ...

2. Walk, hike, stroll and ramble

While cars are great for those rainy Monday mornings when the kids are late for school and you have to do the week's supermarket shopping, try to avoid driving when it's possible to walk. If the walk to school would take fifteen minutes longer but take in some pretty gardens or futuristic office buildings, walk as often as possible so that your children can point things out to you or ask questions about the new things they see, not to mention get some easy exercise. You can always use the time to practise their spelling homework or play word games.

Likewise at weekends, if your children are old (or young) enough to go on long walks without going on strike, walk to your nearest park for some rounders or into town for a hot chocolate. Children might complain at the prospect of a walk but quickly forget to whinge once they're actually outside in the fresh air, and before they know it they've arrived at their destination having had a surprisingly fun stroll. Finding conkers, seeing squirrels, meeting friendly dogs, looking through the windows of impressive sports cars – these are all things you can miss out on by driving.

TOP TIP

If you find your children's energy and enthusiasm beginning to flag, distract them by launching into a game of 'I Spy', asking what sort of topping they want on their ice cream, or awarding ten ultimately meaningless points to the next person who sees a brown car or falling leaf.

3. Have a quiet night in

Once upon a time, BFK, Friday nights were all about going out and having the best night of the week. Even if you had no fixed plans by the end of work on a Friday, you knew that somehow, somewhere, something fun would be going on.

Nowadays, Friday night usually heralds the beginning of a busy weekend of sports practice and birthday parties, so, whenever possible, reclaim Friday night as your own. Get the kids to bed on time and spend the rest of the evening curled up on the sofa with your partner, with wine, candles, popcorn, a DVD ... Whatever would make it a cosy evening for you both.

4. Kiss me, darling

Whether it's in the romantic sense with your husband or in the maternal sense with your family, showing affection benefits everyone. Cuddling your children is as good for you as it is for them, filling both parties with a feeling of warmth, security, love, contentment and happiness.

Equally important is the QT you spend alone with your husband, especially at the end of a long day apart or chasing after children. If you don't have the time or inclination for sex (which, brace yourself, we'll come to in a moment), some intimate time together can be just the tonic. What's more, you burn twenty-six calories for every minute you spend kissing, so you can include it as part of your workout schedule!

3 CLASSIC MOVIES FOR A QUIET NIGHT IN

Choosing a movie that will please both men and women can be rather a nightmare, but check out this trio of fabulous classics for a bit of inspiration:

1. ***The African Queen* (1951):** Set in East Africa at the outbreak of World War One, this movie sees salt-of-the-earth boat captain Humphrey Bogart and prim-and-proper missionary Katharine Hepburn reluctantly travelling downriver together to escape a marauding German army. Despite being completely at odds on most topics, together they hatch a plan to torpedo the Germans' gunboat ... Warm, witty and involving a madcap scheme to alter the course of the war, this is a classic for all tastes.

2. ***An Affair to Remember* (1957):** Another film involving a boat – but this time it's a cross-Atlantic cruise liner. Starring Cary Grant as a dashing international playboy and Deborah Kerr as the enchanting, down-to-earth object of his affections, this movie is funny, sad and romantic all at once, and far better than its 1993 spin-off, *Sleepless in Seattle*.

3. ***Some Like It Hot* (1959):** Boats, trains, swanky hotels, Prohibition-era speakeasies, Marilyn Monroe as a sultry singer, Jack Lemmon and Tony Curtis as cross-dressing musicians escaping the Mafia ... You almost couldn't make it up. This movie really does have something for everyone!

5. Get scribbling

The only time we tend to see handwriting these days is in birthday cards or on shopping lists. We're far more accustomed to receiving brief texts and businesslike emails – it's a wonder we can still string a tidy sentence together at all. The handwritten letter has become virtually extinct, and the lovely letters we would have received from grandparents or pen friends as children are now dealt with electronically.

Well, maybe it's time for a writing revolution! Write a letter to your best friend in Canada, send your husband a funny card at work, or scribble down a joke to slip into your child's lunchbox. These things are so rare these days that the recipient can't help but be surprised to receive something other than a bill via snail-mail. If you see a postcard you know a certain someone would love, why wait for their birthday?

6. Phone a friend

How often do you phone someone for no real reason, just to catch up? It's become the norm to forego phone calls – blame those pesky text messages again – and instead simply drop friends a quick 'Hi, how R U? Mad busy here – must catch up soon! X' every now and then or, worse, assume they're fine since they haven't posted anything to the contrary on Facebook lately.

It's got to the stage where we're actually quite baffled if someone phones for no apparent reason, but the proper catch-up you can have over the phone is worth so much more than a month of abrupt text messages or round-robin emails. If you're worried you'll catch someone in the middle of something important, text them earlier in the day and ask them to let you know when they're free for that long-overdue chat.

TOP TIP

Lengthy and/or long-distance phone calls can be unbelievably expensive, so invest in a cheap online service such as Skype. If you have a webcam, you can even chat face-to-face.

7. Create memories

If you've ever stumbled across your stash of teenage diaries, you'll appreciate that the smallest of prompts can transport you right back to a long-lost moment. It's the same with photo albums that haven't seen the light of day for a few years – remember that awful hairdo you had in 1989 or that unidentifiable meal you were served while backpacking in Bulgaria?

Diaries and albums are wonderful records to look back on, so why not encourage your kids to keep a diary and collect photos of their parties and school trips? You can either create albums online, or, if you don't mind spending a few rainy afternoons with the scissors and glue, of the more old-fashioned variety. Keeping your own diary during the first few years of your child's life can provide many a fond recollection of first words and ridiculous 'but *WHY*?' questions to embarrass them with in years to come.

ORIGINAL IDEAS FOR DELIGHTFUL DATING

We've all been there: on the rare occasion that you and your partner find yourselves at liberty from childminding duties, you have no idea how to spend your 'date'. You may end up at the curry house round the corner or the old-man pub down the road, simply because they're local and hassle-free, but why not try something a little more memorable …

- ★ Do something retro and a bit silly that you enjoyed in younger days, such as ice-skating, bowling or playing arcade games.
- ★ Pretend you're tourists in your nearest city and visit the monuments and parks you've taken for granted for the past few decades.
- ★ Spend a weekend at your nearest seaside town, even if it's a three-hour drive away, and enjoy the beach, the fish and chips and the charmingly ramshackle guesthouses.
- ★ Go to the cinema and watch a really scary or sexy movie – the sort of thing you could never watch with the kids. Plenty of scope for cuddling up in the back row.
- ★ Recreate your first date in all its nervous, awkward glory. For extra authenticity, you could hire your mother to twitch the front-room curtains as your partner 'drops you off' at home.
- ★ Take it in turns to surprise each other – you'll organize this month's date if he sorts out next month's – and try to outdo each other in the imagination and romance stakes.
- ★ Go to your nearest intercity railway station and decide on the spur of the moment which train to jump on. Work out where to stay overnight and what to see once you get there. It's the busy parents' version of backpacking!

EASY CANAPÉS

Finger-food needn't be fussy or elaborate to be a success – and the easier it is to make, the longer you can spend giving the house a once-over and trying on five different outfits. Try your hand at these quick and easy ideas:

Cheats' Blinis

Blinis are mini Russian pancakes that can be bought in most supermarkets, but which are little-used enough to seem almost exotic (compared to sausage rolls, at least).

You will need:

Blinis – two or three per person
Garlic or herb cream cheese – enough to slather each blini
Lemon juice
Chopped chives
Chopped smoked salmon (optional)

Mix the cream cheese with a few drops of lemon juice. If you are using smoked salmon, chop it up into small pieces and throw it into the mix.

Heat the blinis under the grill so that they get slightly crispy and then spread the cream-cheese mix onto them. Garnish with chopped chives and serve on a large platter.

Mozzarella, Tomato and Basil Sticks

Everyone loves a tomato and mozzarella salad, but that's more of a sit-down starter. This is a ridiculously easy, buffet-party variation on the perennial classic.

You will need:

Cherry tomatoes
Mozzarella
Fresh basil leaves
Salt and pepper
Small wooden skewers

Cut the mozzarella into cubes of the same sort of size as the cherry tomatoes. Thread a piece of mozzarella, a basil leaf and a tomato onto each skewer and stick the whole lot under the grill for about two minutes – just enough time for the cheese and tomato to be warm and soft, but not long enough for the mozzarella to become unmanageable. Season with salt and pepper and serve on a platter.

Honey Mustard Glazed Sausages

Dig out the unfinished packet of party sausages you bought for your child's last birthday party. They may not look very glamorous but this recipe has a bit of an adult kick to it, which will make all the difference.

You will need:

Sausages
Honey
Mustard

Mix some honey with a teaspoon or two of English mustard and use the mixture to coat the sausages before heating them in the oven, following the cooking instructions on the packet. The sausages will be lovely and sticky with a hint of spice to them. If you and your friends like a lot of spice, add some Tabasco sauce to the glaze.

8. Cook up a storm

Yes, you have to do it every day when everyone's back from work and school, but there's a huge difference between whipping up a few plates of fish fingers and vegetables and taking the time to prepare something really special. Cooking can be one of the most relaxing household tasks, if you have the uninterrupted time and space to throw yourself into it. There are few things more sensual than slowly putting together a stew, curry or chili con carne, stirring gently and savouring the delicious foody aromas – background music essential and glass of wine optional.

Can't think of a good excuse to get busy in the kitchen just for the hell of it? Simply dig out the flour and get baking! You can never have enough cakes and biscuits in life.

★ Offer to bring a dessert to a friend's forthcoming dinner party – she'll no doubt be delighted not to have to make three courses.

★ Make your own edible Christmas decorations: prepare a batch of thin gingerbread biscuits, using cookie cutters to create Christmassy shapes, and then make a pea-sized hole in the top of each before baking. Once they've cooled, thread some colourful ribbon through the holes and hang on your tree.

TOP TIP

If you routinely avoid cooking a favourite dish because you know the kids won't eat it, make enough for a couple of lunches and freeze the portions in separate containers, ready to pull out and microwave whenever you have the house to yourself.

9. Get it on

OK, I appreciate that you don't need me to tell you that sex is a Good Thing – you've done it before – so I'll keep it brief. But since sex can end up very much on the back burner in the chaotic aftermath of childbirth, it's worth remembering that it's also very good for you...

Sex works every muscle and is especially good for the heart and the lungs, so can be considered a free aerobic workout. It's possible to burn up to 300 calories an hour, making it rather a win-win activity.

Although sex increases blood pressure temporarily, the aerobic workout helps keep your blood pressure down in the long term, thereby reducing the risk of heart disease or stroke.

★ Sex boosts your immune system by increasing the production of the antigen Immunoglobulin A, which helps fight against colds and flu.

★ Just before orgasm, the hormone oxytocin – a natural painkiller and sedative – is released into the body, helping to relieve any aches and pains (such as PMS) and aiding good-quality sleep.

★ The oestrogen produced during sex helps keep your hair shiny and skin glowing.

★ As if further reasons were required, let's face it: sex can be a lot of fun.

MAKING THE FIRST MOVE

No sniggering at the back, now. If sex has fallen down the priorities list, it can be difficult or even quite embarrassing to bring the topic up with your other half. Men don't require an awful lot of persuasion when it comes to sex, though, so something as clichéd-sounding as preparing a candlelit romantic meal or wearing something you know he loves ought to get things rolling.

Turning him on doesn't just happen in the bedroom, either – it can happen when you're in the kitchen with flour on your nose, or when your shoulder strap drops, or when he has a suggestion of what you're wearing underneath (if anything). Sometimes a long, lingering kiss is all that's required. The more spontaneous the better, really – anything too businesslike ('Shall we have sex tonight?') can ruin the mood.

Don't be afraid to put in special requests – it might even be a turn-on – and whatever you do, don't point out your body hang-ups as soon as the clothes are off. Imagine if he started reeling off a list of everything he disliked about his own body! It's not sexy and this is hardly the time for a brutal appraisal of your appearance.

10. Enjoy the seasons

No matter how many seasons we've lived through, we always feel a sense of surprise on the first truly summery day of the year, or at the first snow. The change of seasons always seems so sudden and unexpected, doesn't it? One minute you're struggling home through blustery January rain and next thing you know it's a boiling day in June, perfect for ice creams and games in the park.

Making the most of what each season has to offer is so easy when you have young children – they want nothing more than to make snowmen, pick wild flowers and berries, splash around in the sprinkler and kick fallen leaves and conkers. Treat each perfectly springlike or autumnal day as if it might be the last one this year and do something as a family that, in hindsight, will really sum up that season.

Stress-Proof Your Life

Few things are more guaranteed to transform you from a serene domestic goddess into a harassed mother than stress. Stress is so all-consuming that it can take over your life entirely and give you an irrationally pessimistic outlook; instead of working towards a more manageable way of organizing things, you can find yourself turning the same problems over and over in your head.

One of the likeliest causes of stress is a feeling of helplessness – as if you're being swept along through life with no real control over what happens. The best way to tackle this is by doing a thorough stock-take of your life and arranging things in a more efficient way. This chapter is all about different ways of organizing yourself so as to avoid a bottleneck of unmanageable tasks.

10 STRESS-BUSTING TIPS FOR BUSY MUMS

1. Make lists – elementary level

There's nothing like a 'to-do' list to keep track of all the things you need to achieve on a daily basis. But the problem I found when I gave up work to become a full-time mother was that I ended up with various scrappy lists all over the house. The trick is to have a designated place for your 'to-do' list – whether it's in a diary, Filofax or mobile phone – rather than scribbling things down on the backs of envelopes or urgent letters from the school. Take five minutes at the end of each day to cross off the things you've done and add any new tasks for the next day.

Other rolling lists that prove invaluable are Christmas and birthday-present lists – if you see something during the course of the year and know your child would love it for Christmas, write it down before you forget. Likewise, keep a note of any ideas for fun days out or birthday-party themes that come to you in a flash of inspiration.

TOP 3 KITCHEN TIPS

1. If you don't own a vegetable steamer but fancy steaming your greens for a change, use a metal colander instead. Put the prepared vegetables into the colander, place it on top of a pan of boiling water, and cover the whole lot with a lid. But be careful: it will become very hot.
2. To prevent a smelly bin, put a solid air-freshener in the bottom of the bin (before putting the bag in). It'll keep your kitchen free of rubbishy odours for weeks.
3. Restore shine to a stainless-steel sink and taps by rubbing a touch of vinegar over the surface. Leave for about an hour and then buff with kitchen towel for a shiny finish.

2. Don't be a slave to routine

Some mums live by routine from the moment they get up to the moment they go to bed. While establishing a routine can help create order in a hectic household and is useful for certain things – such as leaving the house on time every morning – it's important to accept that routines, like rules, will be broken every now and then, to avoid becoming anxious when this inevitably happens. If routine were adhered to slavishly, there would never be any time for spontaneous fun or the sort of last-minute changes of plan that become necessary when your child develops toothache and has to stay at home.

Routine can seem the only way to manage when both parents work, but a bit of common sense can make the schedule flow in a less regimented way. Instead of insisting the kids are in bed by 8pm on the dot ('well, you see, they rise at 7am and have to have breakfast by 7.30'), relax things a bit by widening the bedtime window to, say, between 7.45 and 8.30. That way, any unforeseen circumstances shouldn't derail the whole evening and leave you feeling as if you've let things slip. Excitable children and strict schedules simply don't mix well – don't be hard on yourself.

3. Work when you're most productive

When you were at school or university you probably knew exactly whether you were an early bird or night owl, depending on when you were most able to finish your overdue assignments. The same sort of principle applies in motherhood – although hopefully with less of the 'essay-crisis' anxiety. If you tend to be more alert and energetic in the mornings, for example, aim to get the bulk of your work done then, with lighter tasks saved for the afternoon slump, and any tasks that can be fitted around feeding, playing with and washing children saved for the evening. If you're half asleep in the mornings but full of beans after lunch, plan your jobs around that.

Most people's natural body clocks make them feel energized in the mornings until around midday, and then again in the early evening. This is probably the ideal energy-distribution to have, as it gives you the later evening off to relax on the sofa with your partner.

4. Detoxify your surroundings

Whether or not you follow the principles of feng shui when it comes to arranging your furniture and plants, there's a lot to be said for everything having its place. If you're surrounded by clutter and mess as you try to go about your daily jobs, you're bound to become needlessly stressed. Whether it's a permanent pile of papers on the dining room table or a gaggle of worthless ornaments that serve no purpose other than gathering dust, target the clutter and make dealing with it a priority. If the clutter belongs to your partner or a child old enough to know better, it goes without saying that they ought to take responsibility for it.

Are you a hoarder? If you can't bear to part with the various *objets* that are cluttering up your life, invest in some decent storage boxes that can be filled systematically and stored in the garage or under the stairs. Take an extra ten minutes to label each box as accurately as possible – if you can't face sorting out the clutter, at least know where every item or document is.

If, on the other hand, the situation's become so dire that you need a thorough spring clean, try to give everything a designated home and make sure everyone knows about it. Keep paperwork and stationery away from areas they have no business invading – the top of the microwave, for instance – and make it your children's job to put DVDs and computer games back in their cases when they've finished with them, rather than allowing things to pile up into a towering mess.

If you'd like to get spiritual about the clutter, see p.150 for some tips about feng shui.

5. Detoxify your acquaintances

It sounds callous, but yes, you did read that right. I don't mean you should ditch your friends in order to streamline your life; rather, be honest with yourself about the people around you who persistently stress you out or make unmanageable demands on your time and generosity. You know the ones I mean: so-called friends who test your patience but are never there when you need them, or who make snide remarks about your style or size, or who stand you up without explanation or excuse. Over time, being taken for granted – or downright insulted – will take its toll on your general mood and is guaranteed to bring you down.

If you have an acquaintance who fits this category, you need to bite the bullet and discuss the issue with them before you spiral into resentment. It may well be that they have no idea of the effect their attitude has on you. If you feel your friendship isn't strong enough to withstand that kind of frank discussion, the relationship is quite possibly an unhealthy one in any case.

Some mums pick up a lot of acquaintances along the way from pregnancy to childbirth and school – you don't have to become firm friends with them all. If the only common ground you have is your choice of maternity ward, don't feel obliged to maintain a long-lasting relationship.

TOP TIP

Your self-esteem is one of the most vital components of your fabulousness. For the sake of glamour – if not for the sake of your sanity – don't let yourself be brought down by unhealthy friendships.

6. Make lists – advanced level

Do you often run late for appointments? Do you struggle to get the kids to school on time? Do you have to hunt for clean school uniforms amidst a sea of laundry? Are the kids' rooms a mess? Do you have no time to sit down during the day? Does life seem to be utter chaos at times?

If so, it's time to create a more detailed version of your 'to-do' list. Making a realistic agenda of each day's plans will not only help you prioritize but should ultimately free up some break times for you. Experiment with the following plan over a two-week period and see if your stress levels plummet as a result.

Using your organizer of choice (book or computer – not the back of the electricity bill), jot down a list of your weekly household tasks, followed by a list of daily tasks, and then a list of long-term projects. For example:

Weekly tasks
Washing
Ironing
Tidying
Cleaning and dusting
Hoovering
Dry cleaning
Big food shop
Make sure garden's presentable
Keep bills and household and personal admin up to date

Daily tasks
Make breakfast
Prepare packed lunches
School run x 2
Oversee homework
Cook dinner
Get some exercise

Long-term projects
Clear out loft
Learn to drive
Book summer holiday

Now divide your weekly tasks up so that you have one or two each day over the course of the week. Since Monday is such a gloomy day all round, and probably also the day on which your house is messiest, you may as well try to get the cleaning jobs you like least out of the way on Monday. Washes can be done on a rolling basis while you do other things, but perhaps leave those for later in the week so that there are plenty of clean clothes for the weekend. Personally I like to get as much ironing as possible over and done with on Friday so that I don't have to touch the shirts or school uniform over the weekend. I also do another quick tidy and hoover on Friday, so that the house is ready for a weekend of toys being flung all over the place and mud being traipsed through the kitchen.

If you enjoy gardening, you might even see that 'chore' as a break from your indoor tasks, in which case give yourself a couple of gardening sessions each week.

Now that the weekly tasks are taken care of, intersperse them with the things that need to be done daily, giving yourself a realistic amount of time to achieve each task. If you plan on cooking every night, you can save a lot of time by preparing double the amount of certain versatile dishes and freezing them for use in another meal later that week – chili con carne, for instance, can be eaten with rice on Monday and with a jacket potato on Wednesday, and a roast chicken can be used for at least two meals (see p.199). Likewise, if preparing packed lunches in the mornings is liable to make you late for the school run, prepare as much of them as possible the previous evening.

Any long-term tasks can then be broken up and dealt with one chunk at a time – anything that involves lifting a finger should be given a 'worktime' slot and the more fun things can be looked into during your internet/email breaks.

So once you have an idea of what your daily routine consists of on paper, it's now much easier to set your daily agenda. The times here are just given as guidance – remember not to be too strict with your schedule and to give yourself plenty of well earned breaks.

Monday

7am	Wake, shower, dress and tea
7.30	Wake the children and get them ready
8.00	Prepare and eat breakfast
8.30	School run
9.15	Tidy the bedrooms
10.00	Get some fresh air or do an express exercise workout
10.30	Coffee break/check emails
10.45	Clean the bathrooms and hallways
11.45	Hoover the upstairs
12pm	Lunch break
1.00	Clean the living room, dining room and kitchen
2.00	Hoover the downstairs
2.15	Coffee break/look into holidays, jobs or courses
3.00	School run
3.45	Give the kids a snack
4.00	Start preparing dinner while children watch TV/play
5.00	Homework/playtime
6.00	Dinner time
6.45	Bath time
7.15	Story and bed
7.30	Clean up dinner/toys and put a load in the washing machine ready for next morning
8.00	Tick off completed tasks and compile tomorrow's agenda

AND RELAX!

Tuesday

7am	Wake, shower, dress and tea
7.30	Wake the children and get them ready
8.00	Put on the washing and sort out breakfast
8.30	School run
9.15	Do some household and personal admin – pay bills, respond to emails, check bank accounts
10.15	Hang out the washing
10.30	Express exercise workout
10.45	Coffee break
11.00	Put a second wash on and give the front garden a once-over
12pm	Lunch break
1.00	Hang out the washing
1.15	Spend some time clearing out the loft
3.00	School run
3.45	Take the kids to the park
5.00	Homework with the children
6.00	Dinner (the second portion of Sunday's dinner)
6.45	Bath time
7.15	Story and bed
7.30	Clean up dinner/toys
8.00	Tick off completed tasks and compile tomorrow's agenda

RELAX AND HAVE AN EARLY NIGHT

Wednesday

6.30am	Wake and exercise (yoga/Pilates or workout)
7.00	Shower, dress and tea
7.30	Wake children and get them ready
8.00	Sort out breakfast
8.30	School run
9.15	Meet friends at a café or someone's house
11.15	Drop off dry cleaning on way home
11.30	Give the back garden a once-over
12.30pm	Lunch break
1.30	Spend some time online, looking into driving lessons or courses and dealing with emails
3.00	School run
3.45	Prepare a snack for the kids
4.00	Homework and playtime
6.00	Dinner (adapted from Monday's)
6.45	Bath time
7.15	Story and bed
7.30	Clean up dinner/toys and put a load in the washing machine ready for next morning
8.00	Tick off completed tasks and compile tomorrow's agenda

AND RELAX

If you think this is all a bit too regimented, forget allotting certain amounts of time to each task and simply make a list of the major things you want to achieve each day:

Monday
Clean and hoover entire house
Cook dinner

Tuesday
Washing
Admin
Do a bit of clearing in loft
Kids to park

Wednesday
Coffee morning
Gardening
Look up courses/holidays/part-time jobs

TOP TIP

All of these suggested schedules assume your other half and older children aren't willing to lift a finger around the house. If this is the case, turn back to the chapter on confidence and assertiveness!

7. Prioritize

Prioritize the things on your 'to-do' list according to what is most urgent or time-sensitive. If you have a particularly busy week – let's say you're getting ready for a family holiday – the time you might have spent cleaning the house from top to bottom might be better spent ironing and packing cases. The cleaning is a low priority in this situation, and unfortunately will still be there when you get back. Your weekly agenda is just there as a guide, so if there's one particular job that's causing you to worry, address that first and fit the lesser things around it.

8. Embrace Plan B

Even with your various lists and agendas, not everything will go to plan. Say a friend calls you on a Friday morning and suggests meeting for lunch that same day, but you have your ironing and speed-cleaning day ahead of you – what on earth to do? The answer is quite simple: forget the cleaning and fit in the areas most in need of a once-over before and after your lunch, or when you have a few minutes here and there over the weekend. Unless you're expecting a visiting dignitary (the mother-in-law, for instance), the house doesn't have to be entirely spotless every weekend.

If you can't achieve Plan A for whatever reason, embrace Plan B instead. Lord knows there's more to life than rules and routines, so go out and enjoy your lunch date or make the most of some unexpected good weather.

TOP TIP

Approach your Mum Tasks with flexibility and good humour: remember you're in charge, so take control.

9. Have a healthy mind in a healthy body

The Roman poet Juvenal decreed that '*mens sana in corpore sano*' ('a healthy mind in a healthy body') was one of the most desirable things in life, and his advice couldn't be more relevant to busy mums today. If you look after yourself properly, you'll have a more positive outlook on things, which in turn will massively reduce your susceptibility to stress.

So if there's anything in your diet or exercise regimes (or lack of...) that causes you to feel uneasy, uncomfortable or unattractive, try cutting it out. Does that second coffee give you the jitters? Did that late-night piece of cake leave you sleepless and too full of energy? Does your expensive gym membership make you feel guilty every time you skip a session? Cut them out – or substitute them for less stress-inducing things – and see if you feel more energetic and positive.

TOP TIP

Unused gym memberships are one of the most stress-inducing commodities of modern times. If ever it gets to the stage where you've skipped a whole month for no apparent reason but yet you can't see yourself going back any time soon, hold your head up high and quit. Think of all the fabulous fun you could have with the money you save ...

THE WORLD'S BEST SLEEPOVER

So you've finally given in and allowed your child to have a sleepover as part of a birthday party. Unbeknownst to your child, who will expect you to make yourself scarce for the whole night and pretend you can't hear the sounds of midnight feasts and computer games, your behind-the-scenes presence and preparation are what will make the party flow from one fun activity to the next.

There are two golden rules when it comes to hosting the perfect sleepover, which will guarantee that your child's party has the edge over everyone else's.

1. Your child is in charge

Or so he or she must think: meddling mums are no fun at sleepovers.

- ★ Ask your child in advance to help you plan what to serve for dinner and breakfast, picking and choosing from their suggestions the things that you planned to make all along
- ★ Buy or rent a selection of pre-approved movies and tell the kids they can watch whichever ones they want
- ★ Plan how a computer-game championship might easily be organized, working out how many people ought to be in each team and how points systems might work, and get your child to suggest it to the group

2. Relax the rules (for one night only)

Unfortunately, kids tend to consider sleepovers without a midnight feast and a scary movie to have been a total waste of time, so you'll need to come up with a way to let them have their fun without compromising your sanity.

- ★ In preparation for a raid on the kitchen, try to have some decent snacks 'lying around', but avoid anything too sugary or caffeinated if you plan on getting any sleep, or anything in smashable containers that might require urgent clearing-up at 2am
- ★ Do a bit of research to source movies that have just the right level of suspense/action for your child's age group, so that the kids get to watch something exciting but don't go home traumatized
- ★ Accept that there will be chatter throughout the night and only make an appearance in your nightie if the noise becomes unacceptable or is keeping everyone awake

10. Maintain a healthy life-work-play balance

After running with your new daily agenda for a couple of months, you should have some idea of whether or not it's working out for the better. Do you have enough time for your children, your husband, your friends and – most importantly – yourself, or are you still run ragged?

If you feel the balance isn't quite right, make some adjustments based on your personal circumstances. Your household priorities will be affected by whether you have a day job or regular evening commitments, whether you socialize a lot during the day or have some help around the house, and whether your children are out at school or need near-constant attention. The last thing I want is for my stress-busting suggestions to increase your stress levels, so tailor your agenda to your lifestyle and keep tweaking it until it runs like clockwork – albeit with the occasional unexpected cuckoo.

Be a Domestic Goddess

Whether you are a stay-at-home mum or not, running a tight ship will always be a priority, especially with young kids charging around determined to wreak havoc in every room. And while housework doesn't rank highly on most mums' list of Fun Activities, it's one of those necessary evils we all have to deal with. Let's not get too downbeat about it, though – there are loads of easy tips, tricks and illusions to streamline your household chores and transform you from Cinderella to Nigella in no time.

Being a domestic goddess isn't about learning to love the ironing or greeting your husband with a batch of freshly baked muffins every evening, but about feeling confident in your household-management skills. You may not even be very good at certain household tasks – but nobody need ever know.

If you can prepare a series of family meals seemingly effortlessly, all the while looking absolutely stunning as you await your impeccably well-behaved children at the school gates, you'll have achieved the art of the domestic goddess. Just don't tell anyone the secret ...

10-STEP GUIDE TO CREATING THE RIGHT ILLUSIONS

1. What are your strengths and weaknesses?

In order to work out which areas of your domestic life need a touch of magic, make a list of your domestic strengths and weaknesses. Take your time and be brutally honest with yourself – pretend you're taking a lie-detector test.

Your list might start off a bit like this:

Strengths
Ruthless with clutter
Good at following recipes
Good at entertaining
Helpful with homework

Weaknesses
Can't stand gardening
Lazy about washing up
Not an imaginative chef
Disorganized with paperwork

Once you have your lists, you can start thinking about how to play up your strengths to maximum effect and how to improve upon – or disguise – your weaknesses so as not to shatter the domestic-goddess illusion. It'll take time to fine-tune your techniques, but, as my mother rather cryptically likes to say, 'Eat your elephant a bit at a time.' A wise woman, my mother.

Turn to p.211 for some tips and tricks for using your strengths and weaknesses to the best advantage.

2. Make the most of charity shops

A messy home is a sign of a chaotic household – or so some people think. And while true glamour isn't all about what other people think, projecting the right sort of vibes is very important. So, when you feel brave enough to tackle the clutter (see p.180 for more on this), be as ruthless as you can.

Don't try to do the whole house in one go – you'll just end up in a clutter-busting frenzy and start throwing out things you still need. Go methodically through every room and scan every shelf, drawer and railing for items you are hoarding needlessly.

Bedroom

★ Clothing you and your partner haven't worn for a full year – clearly there's a reason why not

★ Uninspiring, unfinished novels lying around on the bedside table

★ Accessories you can no longer stand the sight of

Children's room

★ 'Hand-me-down' clothes you know your youngest will never want to wear

★ Christmas presents they asked for but annoyingly never took to

★ Duvet sets they now consider 'sad' or 'babyish'

Kitchen

- ★ Empty ornamental biscuit tins or pasta jars
- ★ Cappuccino frothers, nutcrackers, duplicate corkscrews and other unused utensils
- ★ Cookery books you have no desire to peruse

Lounge

- ★ Unused ornamental candles gathering dust on the mantelpiece
- ★ Coffee-table books you will never actually open
- ★ DVDs that nobody enjoyed watching

Getting rid of perfectly usable things can be quite a dilemma – what if you suddenly develop a taste for homemade cappuccinos? What if you decide to enter a charity tennis tournament at the kids' school? What if someone throws a 1980s-themed fancy-dress party?

Be honest: saving unused things 'just in case' something very unlikely happens is just an excuse not to part with the clutter you've become used to seeing around. Charity shops will welcome with open arms the things you consider to be surplus to requirements, meaning you don't need to worry about stuffing all your excess possessions under the stairs. Not only will your house suddenly seem much more spacious, but you'll feel a huge sense of achievement at having taken control of your home.

Silver (or 'silver') photo frames given as wedding or christening gifts are among the most common pieces of household 'junk' you may be loathe to chuck out. Be ruthless: can you see yourself ever putting a photo into it and letting it adorn your home? If not, never mind who gave it to you – get rid. Anything that's literally unusable should of course go to the dump.

While you're at the charity shop dropping off your photo frames and old Jilly Cooper novels, have a rummage around for some cheap vintage clothing. There are few things more satisfying in the glamour stakes than announcing you bought your latest on-trend outfit for a fiver.

3. Cook the books

If you don't enjoy cooking or aren't a natural chef, you unfortunately still need to find a way of providing (or contributing towards) a daily meal for the family. Ready meals and takeaways have their place every now and then, but they don't leave you with quite the same sense of achievement as you get from cooking something deceptively simple.

Job 1 is to master a handful of idiot-proof recipes (of which there are loads over the next few pages), and Job 2 is to choose ones that are open to cunning adaptation. Leftover chili, ratatouille, roasted vegetables and roast chicken can all be recycled into surprisingly varied dishes, meaning that you only need to cook a double amount of something on Wednesday in order to have Friday's dinner half-ready. Job 3, of course, is to get your other half to do likewise – a problem shared is a problem halved, after all.

The food recycling you do out of laziness, lack of time or lack of inspiration will be labelled 'thrifty innovation' by your other mum friends, which earns you major domestic-goddess brownie points.

4. Waste not, want not

OK, so here are a few versatile, idiot-proof recipes that ought to see you through for a while. I don't want to put you off by making them sound more complicated than they are – they really are simple – so you won't find milligrams and fluid ounces here. Cooking isn't a precise science – throw in as much of each ingredient as sounds sensible and taste frequently along the way. If the meal looks a bit cobbled-together but tastes fine, you've done a good job.

THREE WAYS WITH LEFTOVER CHICKEN

I won't patronize you by explaining how to roast a chicken – it's fairly straightforward and there are basic instructions on the underside of the packaging – but knowing what to do with the inevitable leftovers is a tip worth passing on.

You can make your Sunday lunch less of a hassle by buying ready-made gravy and even frozen roast potatoes or mash (sounds incredibly lazy but there are some decent varieties out there now), but make up for it by boiling or steaming some lovely fresh vegetables.

Shred the leftover chicken and stick it in the fridge to be used over the next two days. Here are some simple recipe ideas.

Chicken Supreme

You will need:

Olive oil
Onion, finely chopped
Shredded chicken – a large handful per person
White sauce – homemade if you know how but it's easily available in shops
Rice – cooked as per packet instructions
French green beans
Parmesan, grated – optional

Gently fry the onion in a little olive oil and then add the shredded chicken, tossing for a few minutes to warm it through. Add the white sauce and turn off the heat once it starts to bubble. Serve with rice and the steamed green beans (you can steam the beans over the rice), and with Parmesan sprinkled on top if you choose.

Chicken and Garlic Pasta

You will need:

Pasta
Olive oil
Shredded chicken – a handful per person
Fresh peas, defrosted a little
Garlic cream cheese, and lots of it
Green veg of your choice

Boil the pasta of your choice. Heat a little olive oil in a large frying pan and then add the chicken and peas. Cook for just a few minutes until heated through and then add the garlic cream cheese – as much as you need to coat everything properly. Once cooked through, add to the cooked pasta and serve with green beans or broccoli.

Chicken Pitta Kebabs with Hummus

You will need:

Pitta bread – one per person, unless anyone's particularly ravenous
Shredded chicken – warm or cold, depending on the season
Mixed salad – lettuce, red peppers, thinly sliced cucumber
Chili sauce (optional)
Hummus

Take your lightly heated pitta bread and split open. Fill with chicken and salad, adding chili sauce if you like. Serve with a generous dollop of hummus.

TOP TIP

Roasting a chicken, though simple enough, can be relatively time-consuming, what with preparing the roasting tray, checking on its progress, carving the thing up once it's done. If you anticipate being able to make use of lots of leftovers during the week – in soups, sandwiches and pasta dishes – roast two chickens side by side at the same time and get all the cooking and carving out of the way in one fell swoop.

VARIATIONS ON THE THEME OF BOLOGNESE

Leftover Bolognese is surprisingly easy to adapt into a number of other dishes, from the slightly bland and child-friendly to spicier, adults-only meals. Start off by making a huge serving of Bolognese to accompany spaghetti.

Spaghetti Bolognese

You will need:

Olive oil
Onion, chopped
Tomato purée
Minced beef or lamb – enough for two meals
Chopped mushrooms
Large jar of passata or ready-made Bolognese sauce
Spaghetti
Parmesan or grated cheese

Heat a little olive oil and throw in the onion with two teaspoons of tomato purée. Stir for a few minutes before adding the minced meat and then cook for about 20 minutes, stirring occasionally so it doesn't all stick together. Throw in the mushrooms, followed by the passata or Bolognese sauce. Let this simmer for about 45 minutes with the lid on. Once cooked, remove half of the mixture, leave to cool, and store it in a sealed container in the fridge. Serve the rest with spaghetti and top with cheese.

Quick and Easy Lasagne

You will need:
Leftover Bolognese mix
Lasagne pasta sheets
Cheese sauce – shop-bought is fine
Grated cheese

Pour about a third of your chilled Bolognese mix into an ovenproof dish, followed by a layer of pasta sheets and a layer of cheese sauce, and continue making these layers until you've run out of meat or space. Top with cheese sauce and a generous scattering of grated cheese. Cover with foil (don't let it touch the cheese, though) and place in the oven at 200°C/Gas Mark 6 for approximately 45 minutes. Serve with mixed salad.

Exotic Shepherd's Pie

You will need:
Leftover Bolognese mix
Mashed potato
Cheese, grated

Stick the Bolognese in a deep, ovenproof dish and cover with mashed potato. Sprinkle some grated cheese on top and cook in the oven at 200°C/Gas Mark 6 for about 25 minutes, or until the meat is warmed through and the potato looks a little crispy on top. Serve with fresh peas and carrots.

Easy Chili Con Carne

You will need:

Leftover Bolognese mix
Splash or three of red wine
Rinsed kidney beans
Chili powder
Rice – cooked as per packet instructions

This is one for you and your partner to eat while the children have something more kid-friendly. Heat the Bolognese mix in a saucepan, adding a few splashes of red wine to flavour it and to add a little liquid. Once it's bubbling a bit, add the kidney beans and as much chili powder as you can stand, and cook until done. You may need to keep adding the odd splash of wine to stop it becoming too dry. Serve with rice and a side salad.

TOP TIP

If your leftover Bolognese mix becomes a bit sticky in the fridge, mix in a small amount of water before reusing it.

MISCELLANEOUS PASTAS, PIES AND PIZZAS

Pasta and noodles are incredibly versatile, taste completely different depending on what they're served with, and, what's more, kids can't get enough of them. Use different pasta shapes to fool your children into thinking it's something new and exciting each time.

Likewise, pies and pizzas are perennial winners when it comes to pleasing the kids, and if you can do something just a little bit different with them – letting them help you make a homemade pizza, for instance – they'll think you're the world's most ingenious mum.

Easy Macaroni Cheese

You will need:
Macaroni
Cheese sauce
Mustard – 1 teaspoon
Grated cheese
Sliced tomato

Boil the macaroni as per instructions, and then strain it. Mix in the cheese sauce and mustard, place the whole lot in an oven-proof dish and sprinkle with grated cheese and sliced tomatoes. Cook in the oven at 200°C/Gas Mark 6 for 20 minutes, until golden on top, and serve with salad.

Tuna Bake Pie

You will need:
Peppers – red, yellow and green
Tuna – 2 regular tins
Sweetcorn – 1 small tin
Mashed potato – a decent amount per person
Mustard – 1 teaspoon
Grated cheese

Cut the peppers into small pieces and drain the tuna and sweetcorn. Mix them all together in an oven-proof dish with the mashed potato and mustard, and sprinkle the top with grated cheese. Cook in the oven at 200°C/Gas Mark 6 for about 25 minutes or until it's nice and crispy on top and heated throughout. Serve with fresh green beans or peas.

Prawn Stir-Fry and Noodles

You will need:

Noodles
Olive oil
A pack of stir-fry vegetables
Fresh or frozen prawns
Jar of sauce (optional)

Boil a large pan of water for the noodles and follow the instructions on the pack. Take a large frying pan – or wok, if you have one – and heat some oil until very hot. Throw in the prawns and vegetables, and add salt and pepper to taste. This will all cook quite quickly, so once they look done (test the prawns to make sure they're cooked through), add the noodles and toss together. Stir in a sauce of your choosing – sweet and sour, plum, black bean or yellow bean.

Oven-Steamed Salmon

You will need:

Salmon fillets – 1 per person, or cook double so as to make the next dish really quick and easy
Olive oil
Lemon juice
Baby tomatoes
Onion, thinly sliced
Garlic, thinly sliced
New potatoes
Green beans

Place the salmon fillets in a baking tray and pour over a little olive oil and lemon juice, along with baby tomatoes, thinly sliced onion and garlic, and salt and pepper to taste. Cover with foil and put in the oven at 190°C/Gas Mark 5 for between 20 and 30 minutes. The salmon will cook in its own steam. Serve with boiled new potatoes and green beans.

Salmon and Broccoli Creamy Pasta

You will need:

Olive oil
Broccoli, broken up into small florets
Flaked cooked salmon (leftover from recipe above)
Crème fraîche
Penne, cooked as per packet instructions
Parmesan

Put a touch of olive oil in a pan and add the small florets of broccoli and the flaked salmon, and cook for a few minutes before adding the crème fraîche. Once it's heated through, pour it over the cooked penne and sprinkle on some Parmesan.

Pizza Baguettes

You will need:

French bread – a long baguette cut into four sections or a number of smaller loaves
Tomato purée or red pesto
Mixed herbs
Grated cheese
Slices of ham or pepperoni (optional)

Perfect for evenings when the kids have clubs. Slice the pieces of bread lengthways. Spread the purée or pesto on them and then sprinkle on some herbs before generously covering with grated cheese. Put them under the grill for a few minutes until they're bubbling and turning golden. If using ham or pepperoni, add this as soon as the cheese has started melting. Serve with salad.

5. Plan ahead

Now that you have a handful of nutritious and delicious recipes at your disposal, spend a few minutes planning the rotation of meals over the next few weeks. Some families operate a weekly rotation of meals – every Monday is pizza, every Thursday is stew – so that everyone knows what's coming up on any given night. This could get rather mundane, though, and is a sure-fire way to make your kids go off certain meals. If you can introduce a two- or three-week plan, making the most of your cunningly recycled dishes, you'll make preparing a series of different meals look incredibly easy.

Based on the recipes over the previous few pages, your three-week plan might look something like this.

Week 1

Sunday	Roast Chicken
Monday	Spaghetti Bolognese
Tuesday	Chicken Supreme
Wednesday	Exotic Shepherd's Pie
Thursday	Pizza Baguette
Friday	Prawn Stir-Fry and Noodles
Saturday	Take-out

Week 2

Sunday	Oven-Steamed Salmon
Monday	Roast Chicken
Tuesday	Salmon and Broccoli Creamy Pasta
Wednesday	Chicken Pitta Kebabs with Hummus
Thursday	Tuna Bake Pie
Friday	Take-out
Saturday	Macaroni Cheese

Week 3

Sunday	Roast Chicken
Monday	Spaghetti Bolognese
Tuesday	Chicken and Garlic Pasta
Wednesday	Lasagne or Chili Con Carne
Thursday	Prawn Stir-Fry and Noodles
Friday	Pizza Baguette
Saturday	Take-out

Obviously you can substitute any of these for your own favourite recipes. The fact of reusing certain bulk ingredients will save you time and money at the supermarket and also means you can put the evening's dinner plans on hold until tomorrow if something last-minute comes up.

TOP TIP

Always have a couple of pizzas and other easy meals stashed in the freezer. You never know when you might have to attend a parent-teacher meeting, look after the neighbours' kids or spend the afternoon in A&E, all of which will leave you less time and energy for cooking.

6. Create the right illusions

At the beginning of this chapter I suggested making a list of your strengths and weaknesses, the purpose of which was to help you create the right illusions about your domestic-goddess status. These are the strengths and weaknesses I gave as an example:

Strengths
Ruthless with clutter
Good at following recipes
Good at entertaining
Helpful with homework

Weaknesses
Can't stand gardening
Lazy about washing up
Not an imaginative chef
Disorganized with paperwork

In many cases, you'll probably find that some of your weaknesses are balanced out by your strengths: *Not an imaginative chef* but *Good at following recipes* and *Good at entertaining*; *Lazy about washing up* and *Disorganized with paperwork* but *Ruthless with clutter*.

Based on these qualities, there are a number of things you could do to create the right impression about your domestic skills ...

- ★ Hone one really impressive dish, following the recipe to the letter. Practise it on your husband and, once you've got it right, unleash it on a series of dinner-party guests. Nobody but the two of you need ever know you've recycled the same dinner for a number of occasions. Keep a note of who's eaten that meal and who hasn't, though! Once the meal has run its course, master a new one.
- ★ Enlist your older children as helpers on the night, offering them a fiver each to load the dishwasher and scrape left-overs into the bin. The children will think they've won the lottery and your guests will be amazed by the clean state of the kitchen at the end of the evening.
- ★ Use one of your under-stairs storage boxes to pile in any unsorted paperwork. Once the evening is over, restore the pile to its rightful place on the dining room table.

7. Perfect your window dressing

We don't like to admit it, but we are all suckers for persuasive packaging. Whether it's a gold-rimmed wine label or a shiny red car, something that's been designed for maximum impact is far more desirable than something that just looks ordinary.

The same applies when it comes to our homes: if they are presented well, we instantly give off an air of success and good living, even if everything has literally just been stuffed under the stairs for the day. It's all about creating the right impression.

The good news is that you don't actually have to polish every item of furniture in your house before someone pops round for a cuppa. A few strategic ruses will suffice to give off a really homely feel:

★ Make sure your driveway and front garden are presentable – empty flowerbeds are better than flowerbeds full of dead plants and weeds

★ Make sure the light bulbs in your hallway and staircase are working

★ If your front curtains have seen better days, tie them back

★ Check there's loo roll, soap and a clean towel in the nearest bathroom

★ Spend fifteen minutes giving the room in which you intend to host a thorough once-over

★ Have fresh coffee or bread smells wafting through the house – it's an old trick but it works wonders

★ If you have a dog, make sure it's presentable and not muddy or smelly – or, if you know your guest is terrified of dogs, keep it at a safe distance

TOP TIP

Essentially, imagine your guests are would-be buyers coming to view the house. What will they see, hear and smell when they walk in?

8. Have impeccably behaved children

It's no good having a spotless house and a finely tuned dinner-party routine if your children are going to behave like monsters all evening and force your guests to flee the scene. Fortunately, your impeccable organizational skills will free up a lot more time to spend with the kids, making sure they get enough fresh air, exercise and mental stimulation to keep them in good humour.

You're a mother and have no doubt honed various techniques for keeping your children entertained and well behaved, so I'll keep this brief. Here are a few suggestions for inexpensive ways in which you could give your kids the edge over other people's offspring:

★ When it comes to traditionally gender-specific activities such as football or horse riding, mix things up a bit. There's no reason why your daughter shouldn't try out some muddy games while your son pretends to be a cowboy.

★ In the same vein, encourage your husband to spend a day alone with any daughters while you take care of your sons. Too often activities get pigeonholed into things for boys or girls only. You might be surprised by what they enjoy.

★ Indulge their passions – cars, dinosaurs, writing stories – by looking up relevant exhibitions, matches or half-term clubs you can attend together. Talk to them about the things they love and ask questions in a way that makes them feel they've really mastered something and made you proud.

★ Don't worry if it's a miserable day, you have no particular inspiration and the kids just want to watch TV or a movie. Knowing what's going on in the world of popular TV is something your kids will be able to discuss with classmates – in the grand scheme of things, it's probably worse for them to be uninformed.

★ Do insist on good manners and pull them up when they forget to say 'please' or 'thank you'. If they need persuading that politeness is a good idea, tell them that they're more likely to get the things they want in life if they go about it in a nice way.

9. Have a helping hand

As your children get older, you can gradually teach them to take on ever more little tasks around the house. This will not only help them develop a sense of responsibility as they grow up, but will also go a long way towards giving them an appreciation of the jobs you do for them daily.

Here are some examples of the things you might ask children of various ages to take responsibility for.

Age 4–7
Helping you choose them the most appropriate outfit for the day ahead
Dressing themselves
Clearing toys/games away at the end of the day
Laying the table

DIPLOMATIC FEEDBACK FOR A CRINGE-WORTHY SCHOOL PLAY

We've all been there: a garishly lit school stage, far too many elaborately costumed children running around at once, someone crying noisily in the wings, half the actors mysteriously wearing clothes pinched from your wardrobe … And then suddenly, mercifully, it's over. But what's this? Your child wants to know what you thought? Help!

What you need is a stockpile of diplomatic phrases, carefully chosen and suitably complimentary or non-committal. Try some of these next time you find yourself put on the spot after yet another catastrophic school play.

★ Well, that was certainly unlike anything I've seen before in my life.

★ I particularly enjoyed the end.

★ Oh, who needs lines? I've always thought the fourth shepherd was the true hero of the Christmas story.

★ It was just like a night at the West End – especially when that food fight broke out between the parents at the back.

★ Your costume was great!

★ You were so much better than that boy who ran out of the hall in tears.

★ Well yes, your little sister *did* make a very realistic Baby Jesus – but how on earth did she get here? Where's the babysitter?

- ★ The interval drinks were an inspired idea.
- ★ Your ad-libbing was very inventive, darling. Where did you learn those interesting words, by the way?
- ★ What a brave new take on the Nativity! I never knew there were vampires in Bethlehem.

Age 7–9
Washing themselves
Cleaning their own rooms
Helping with washing up once a week
Helping with easy dinner preparations

Age 10–12
Folding away all clean laundry
Helping with more complicated dinner preparations
Watering the garden
Being in charge of feeding any pets

If this sounds a bit regimented, fast-forward to your young kids' teenage years, when they may end up lounging around listening to music, refusing to lift a finger, while you mop and cook around them. So help yourself now and you'll also be helping them turn into caring, responsible adults one day.

10. Don't sweat the small stuff

As a glamorous mother, it's important to focus on the things that actually matter, and to let anything extraneous go. If there's something you wish you could do – bake the perfect cake, for example – but it just never works out for you, give it up and hone a different skill instead. Never be afraid to try new things, but know when to transfer your energy to something else instead.

Important
Feeling confident about your appearance
Polite, happy children
Maintaining honest, fun friendships and relationships
A homely home
Being well informed
An efficient (or efficient-seeming) household

Not important
Gourmet cookery skills
The latest fashions
Attending every social engagement you're invited to
Going on expensive holidays
Wearing pearls, dresses and heels every day
Strict schedules and timetables

TOP 10 HANDBAG MUST-HAVES FOR THE GLAMOROUS MUM

1. **Small bottle of water.** Good for your skin, good for your breath, good for your general mood … An all-round lifesaver.
2. **Paperback book.** For those spare ten minutes here and there throughout your working day.
3. **Important phone numbers.** Whether you need to notify the school that you're stuck in hideous traffic or make a last-minute appointment with the dentist, having all your important numbers to hand will save a whole lot of time and stress.
4. **On-the-go make-up kit.** Blusher, lippy, mascara, tweezers, hand cream and a compact mirror – all you need to top up your fabulousness when you're out and about.
5. **Kid-friendly snack.** Something small, vaguely healthy and deceptively tasty – a breakfast bar, for instance – for those urgent pangs of hunger to which bored kids are prone.
6. **Miniature perfume spray.** You never know when you'll be called in for an after-school meeting with your child's dashing maths teacher.
7. **Homemade face spritzer.** For a quick pick-me-up during a busy day or gruelling shopping trip (see p.129).
8. **Notebook.** For jotting down inspiring fashion and beauty ideas as well as ideas for forthcoming birthday and Christmas presents.
9. **A distinctive accessory.** Something fabulous – a colourful neckerchief or feature necklace – for those terrible moments when you find yourself wearing the same outfit as a rival mum.
10. **Wet wipes.** Where would humanity be without them?

Further Fabulous Reading

BOOKS

Absolutely Organized: A Mom's Guide to a No-Stress Schedule and a Clutter-Free Home, Debbie Lillard (North Light Books, 2008)

Afternoon Tea, Jane Pettigrew (Pitkin, 2004)

The Best Friends' Guide to Surviving the First Year of Motherhood, Vicki Iovine (Bloomsbury, 1999)

Brilliant Life Coach: 10 Inspirational Steps to Transform Your Life, Annie Lionnet (Pearson Education, 2008)

The Family Book: Amazing Things to Do Together, Michele Brown (Michael O'Mara Books, 2007)

Feel Fab Forever: The Anti-Ageing Health & Beauty Bible, Sarah Stacey and Josephine Fairley (Kyle Cathie, 2002)

The Little Book of Champagne Cocktails (Hamlyn, 2002)

The Mums' Book: For the Mum Who's Best at Everything, Alison Maloney (Michael O'Mara Books, 2007)

NLP Workbook: A Practical Guide to Achieving the Results You Want, Joseph O'Connor (Thorsons, 2001)

Style Clinic: How to Look Fabulous All the Time, at Any Age, for Any Occasion, Paula Reed (Collins, 2009)

The Wives' Book: For the Wife Who's Best at Everything, Alison Maloney (Michael O'Mara Books, 2008)

The 21st Century Beauty Bible, Sarah Stacey and Josephine Fairley (Kyle Cathie, 2002)

101 Ways to Simplify Your Life: How to Declutter Your Mind, Body and Soul, Suzannah Olivier (Cico Books, 2003)

1001 Little Beauty Miracles: Secrets and Solutions from Head to Toe, Esme Floyd (Carlton Books, 2006)

ONLINE EXPERTS

A collection of fabulous magazines on one brilliant site: www.allaboutyou.com

Cookery tips and how-to video guides on all manner of marvellous topics: www.videojug.com

Eyebrow expert Shavata: www.shavata.co.uk

Family health information: www.boots.com

Fashion, beauty and well-being tips, as well as celebrity fabulousness: www.handbag.com or www.style.com

Hair expertise and guidance: www.ukhairdressers.com

Parenting with style: www.juniormagazine.co.uk

Recipes and entertaining: www.uktv.co.uk/food or www.womanandhome.com

Go forth and be fabulous!